Higher

English

2001 Exam
Close Reading
Analysis and Appreciation

2002 Exam
Close Reading
Analysis and Appreciation

Specimen Question Paper
(for exams in and after 2003)
Close Reading
Critical Essay

2003 Exam
Close Reading
Critical Essay

2004 Exam
Close Reading
Critical Essay

Leckie x Leckie

First exam published in 2001.

Published by Leckie & Leckie, 8 Whitehill Terrace, St. Andrews, Scotland KY16 8RN tel: 01334 475656 fax: 01334 477392 enquiries@leckieandleckie.co.uk www.leckieandleckie.co.uk

Leckie & Leckie Project Team: Andrea Collington; Peter Dennis; Bruce Ryan

ISBN 1-84372-237-2

A CIP Catalogue record for this book is available from the British Library.

Printed in Scotland by Scotprint.

Leckie & Leckie is a division of Granada Learning Limited, part of ITV plc.

Acknowledgements

Leckie & Leckie is grateful to the copyright holders, as credited, for permission to use their material. Every effort has been made to trace the copyright holders and to obtain their permission for the use of copyright material. Leckie & Leckie will gladly receive information enabling them to rectify any error or omission in subsequent editions.

Palgrave Macmillan for an extract from *Lost in Music* by Giles Smith (2002 Close Reading p 3);
The Times for the article 'Warming Up For The Ice Age' by Angus Clark © NI Syndication, London (2000) (2003 SQP Close Reading p 2);
The article 'We Have Been Here Before' by Anne Karpf taken from the *Guardian* June 2002 © Anne Karpf (2003 Close Reading p 3);
The article 'Protective Parents, yes. But Paranoid?' by Catherine Bennett © the *Guardian* (2004 Close Reading p 3).

The following companies/individuals have very generously given permission to reproduce their copyright material free of charge:

Extract from *I'm a Little Special – a Muhammed Ali Reader* by Gerald Early published by Yellow Jersey Press. Used by permission of the Random House Group Limited (2001 Close Reading p 3);
'Originally' is taken from *The Other Country* by Carol Ann Duffy published by Anvil Press Poetry in 1990 (2001 Analysis and Appreciation p 2);
Extract from *Big Bangs* by Howard Goodall published by Chatto & Windus. Used by permission of The Random House Group Limited (2002 Close Reading p 2);
The article 'Can Britain Afford to Keep Talented Immigrants Out?' by Ruth Wishart courtesy of *The Herald* © Newsquest Media Group (2003 Close Reading p 2);
The article 'Is Paranoid Parenting the Greatest Danger to our Kids?' by Melanie Reid courtesy of *The Herald* © Newsquest Media Group (2004 Close Reading p 2).

2001 HIGHER

X039/301

NATIONAL
QUALIFICATIONS
2001

TUESDAY, 15 MAY
9.00 AM – 10.30 AM

ENGLISH AND COMMUNICATION
HIGHER
Close Reading

You should attempt all questions.

The total value of the Paper is 60 marks.

There are TWO passages and questions.

Read both passages carefully and then answer all the questions which follow. **Use your own words whenever possible and particularly when you are instructed to do so.**

You should read each passage to:

understand what the authors are saying about Muhammed Ali (**Understanding—U**);

analyse their choices of language, imagery and structures to recognise how they convey their points of view and contribute to the impact of the passages (**Analysis—A**);

evaluate how effectively each writer has achieved his purpose (**Evaluation—E**).

A code letter (U, A, E) is used alongside each question to give some indication of the skills being assessed. The number of marks attached to each question will give some indication of the length of answer required.

SCOTTISH
QUALIFICATIONS
AUTHORITY

PASSAGE 1

Journalist, Ian Wooldridge, reflects on the life of Muhammed Ali in an article which appeared in the British Airways magazine High Life *in 2000. It is slightly adapted.*

THE GREATEST VICTIM

I first set eyes on Muhammed Ali in the beautiful Palazzo dello Sport in Rome on a September evening in 1960. His name then was Cassius Clay. He was 18 years old, incredibly handsome, about
5 to fight for the Olympic light-heavyweight title and looked scared of nothing. This was the first of a myriad of misconceptions and contradictions about the extraordinary man, who 40 years later was overwhelmingly voted the greatest sportsman
10 of the 20th century.

The truth was that he was dead scared of flying. Two months earlier, on his way to the U.S. boxing trials, he had been violently buffeted during a turbulent flight across to California. It was the
15 first time he had travelled by air and he swore he would never fly again. This was marginally inconvenient when he was one of the hottest hopes America had for Olympic boxing gold. It took hours of persuasion and cajolery to talk him back
20 on to the plane to Italy.

I have often wondered whether the world would have heard of him had he dug his heels in on the day of departure. Probably not. In 1960, in racist, reactionary, bigoted small-town America, uppity
25 young black men were lucky enough to get one break, let alone two.

Destiny determined otherwise. A legend was in the making. What overwhelms you about this man from such a violent trade are the goodness,
30 sincerity and generosity that have survived a lifetime of controversy, racial hatred, fundamental religious conversion, criminal financial exploitation, marital upheavals, revilement by many of his own nation and, eventually, the
35 collapse of his own body.

Little did I visualise, 37 years after that Roman evening, I would meet him again and be reduced to tears. The supreme athlete and unique showman once deemed by *Time* magazine to be the most
40 instantly recognised human being in the world, struggled up from a settee, tottered unsteadily across the carpet and embraced me in an enveloping bear-hug. Facially bloated, he could speak only in brief, almost unintelligible gasps.
45 Reminiscence was impossible. He smiled a lot, but he suffers from narcolepsy as well as the brain damage which some have identified as Parkinson's disease. Every few minutes he slept while his fourth wife, Lonnie, took over the conversation. A
50 little girl in 1960, living in the same street as the Olympic hero and holding a torch for him, she stepped in thirty years later when, health gone and

asset-stripped by rapacious promoters, he was on the skids.

How did Ali, the icon of world sport, come to this? 55
It was a cavalier attitude to money when it was plentiful, an almost childlike trust in the untrustworthy and, throughout, an utterly reckless generosity. One fight I attended in Kuala Lumpur, Malaysia, showed a fascinating insight 60
into how the money haemorrhaged. He was accompanied by a retinue of 44, of whom perhaps six were professionally involved. The rest were relatives, friends of relatives, old pals of Ali who had fallen on hard times, and outright leeches. 65
Daily they plundered the hotel's shopping mall amassing clothes, jewellery and tacky souvenirs, all charged to Ali's account. But there were also altruistic courtiers. Two days before the fight, I was visited by one Charlie Perkins, an ex-Everton 70
footballer I knew slightly. He is an Australian Aborigine, extremely articulate and an evangelist for Aboriginal rights. Charlie had a simple objective—to persuade Ali to fly down to Australia and throw his personality and enormous influence 75
behind their cause. Ali was sympathetic but, no, he would not proceed to Australia. What he did was to put Perkins (and his companions) on his payroll in some spurious capacity and pick up the tab for their airfares back to Sydney. He never met them again. 80
And mainstream America's rejection? He was a national hero on his return to Louisville from his Olympic triumph, but there were still those who called him "boy" and restaurants which didn't admit blacks. Disillusioned, his riposte was 85
to jettison the name Cassius Clay, handed down from the slave owners of his African forebears, and become Muhammed Ali, pilgrim of Mecca, convert to the Muslim faith. It was a predictable decision but one which was to bring opprobrium 90
upon him nationwide. To much of middle-class America he was now a renegade and soon became a pariah when he refused the draft to fight for his country in Vietnam. "I ain't got no quarrel with them Vietcong," he said, and was subsequently, at the 95
peak of his career, banned from boxing for four years.

I am not a boxing expert. Those who are, mostly endorse Muhammed Ali's opinion of himself at his peak: "The Greatest." But it took a long time for 100
mainstream America to become reconciled to that judgement. For many, he was a turbulent, disturbing figure who challenged homespun values.

105 But then eventually there came a night when he won over most of the remaining doubters. It was the best kept secret of the 1996 Olympic Games in Atlanta, at the very heart of America's Deep South, when he emerged high in the tower of the stadium, to extend
110 a trembling arm and apply, just, a flaming torch to light the Olympic cauldron.

Three years later, he was honoured as the Sports Personality of the Millennium, and we held our breath as he struggled with a few words to an
115 adoring audience. The following evening at a dinner, I sat next to him. Having met everyone in the room, he slumbered throughout most of the proceedings. But I had learned to cope with it now, knowing that in his waking moments he could understand everything you said while unable to reply 120 coherently. I had left a pen lying on the table. Ali picked it up and began to doodle on the linen cloth with nursery drawings. "Skyscraper," he whispered. "Airplane." There were six or seven of them and when he'd finished we whipped the cloth from the 125 table and auctioned it on the spot for £10,300 for charity. Muhammed Ali beamed at that. The man who had let millions slip through his fingers knew he was still helping those even less fortunate than himself. 130

PASSAGE 2

The passage is adapted from the introduction to I'm a Little Special—a Muhammed Ali Reader. *Gerald Early considers his feelings in the 1960s about his boyhood hero.*

THE GREAT ALI

I was no good at wood-working and the like, so I saved my paper route money, and simply bought a baseball bat, a genuine Louisville Slugger, the first one I ever owned. I sanded that bat, re-stained it
5 dark, gave it a name. I carved, scratched really, into the bat the word, *Ali*. I tried to carve a lightning bolt but my limited artistic skill would not permit it. I wanted to carry it in a case but I didn't have one. I just slung it over my shoulder like the great
10 weapon it was, my knight's sword. And I felt like some magnificent knight, some great protector of honour and virtue, whenever I walked on the field.

I used that bat the entire summer and a magical season it was. I was the best hitter in the
15 neighbourhood. Once, I won a game in the last at-bat with a home run, and the boys just crowded round me as if I were a spectacle to behold, as if I were, for some small moment, in this insignificant part of the world, playing this meaningless game,
20 their majestic, golden prince.

But, the bat broke. Some kid used it without my permission. He hit a foul ball and the bat split, the barrel flying away, the splintered handle still in the kid's hands.

25 That was 1966 and Muhammed Ali seemed not simply the best boxer of the day but the best boxer who could possibly be imagined—so good that it was an inspiration to see even a picture of him. My body shivered when I saw him as if an electric shock
30 had pulverised my ability to feel. No fighter could touch him. His self-knowledge was glorious, so transcendently fixed was he on the only two subjects he knew: himself and boxing. He so filled me with his holy spirit that whenever, late in a game, our side needed a rally, I would call out Ali's 35 chant to my teammates, "Float like a butterfly sting like a bee!" That made little sense metaphorically in relation to baseball, but it seemed to work more often than not. It was for me, the summer of 1966, Ali's absolute moment of 40 black possibilities fulfilled. And I wanted that and had it for a moment, too, had it, perhaps, among the neighbourhood guys, the touch and glory of the great Ali.

When the bat broke, it seemed a certain spell was 45 broken, too. I drifted away from baseball by steps and bounds. The next summer, 1967, Ali was convicted of draft-dodging. Martin Luther King came out against the Vietnam War. Baseball did not seem very important. Something else was. For you 50 see, I could never be sure, before that spring when Ali first refused to be drafted, if in the end he really would refuse an unjust fight. So when he did finally refuse, I felt something greater than pride: I felt as though my honour as a black boy had been 55 defended, my honour as a human being. He was the grand knight, after all, the dragon-slayer. And I felt myself, little inner-city boy that I was, his apprentice to the grand imagination, the grand daring. The day that Ali refused the draft, I cried in 60 my room. I cried for him and for myself, for my future and his, for all our black possibilities. If only I could sacrifice like that, I thought. If only I could sacrifice my life like Muhammed Ali . . .

Questions on Passage 1

Marks | Cod

1. (*a*) By referring to lines 1–6 ("I first . . . scared of nothing."), briefly explain two things which attracted the writer to Cassius Clay. Use your own words as far as possible in your answer.

2 | U

(*b*) Briefly explain the "first" (line 6) contradiction about Cassius Clay referred to in lines 6–11 ("This was . . . of flying.").

1 | U

(*c*) "This was marginally inconvenient . . . boxing gold." (lines 16–18)

What tone is adopted by the writer in this sentence? Go on to explain briefly how effective you find this tone in the context.

2 | A/E

2. Look at lines 21–35.

(*a*) Explain what the writer means by "Destiny determined otherwise." (line 27)

2 | U

(*b*) Show how the writer uses sentence structure in lines 21–35 to dramatise his view about destiny and Muhammed Ali.

4 | A

3. By referring to lines 36–44, show how the writer uses contrast to convey his shock at meeting Muhammed Ali years later.

2 | A

4. (*a*) Explain in your own words two reasons for Muhammed Ali's poverty. In your answer, you should refer to lines 55–59 ("How did . . . reckless generosity.").

2 | U

(*b*) Show how effective you find the writer's use of imagery to convey his feelings about what happened to Muhammed Ali's money. In your answer, you should analyse two examples from lines 59–68 ("One fight . . . Ali's account.").

4 | A/E

(*c*) What makes Charlie Perkins's motives different from those of Ali's other "courtiers" (line 69)?

2 | U

5. Summarise the main reasons for "mainstream America's rejection" of Muhammed Ali. You should refer to lines 81–104 in your answer and use your own words as far as possible.

5 | U

6. Show how **either** of the final two paragraphs effectively illustrates both the "triumph" and the "tragedy" of Muhammed Ali. You should refer to content and style in your answer.

4 | A/E

(30)

Questions on Passage 2

7. (*a*) By referring to lines 1–8 ("I was . . . have one."), briefly explain how any two of the writer's actions show the importance of the baseball bat to him.

2 | U

(*b*) Show how the writer uses imagery in lines 9–20 ("I just . . . golden prince.") to convey how the bat affected the way he thought about himself. You should refer to two examples in your answer.

4 | A

8. Show how the writer's language in lines 21–24 conveys the impact of the destruction of his bat.

2 | A

9. By referring to lines 25–44, show how the writer uses word choice to convey the intensity of his feelings about Muhammed Ali.

4 | A

10. (*a*) By referring to the final paragraph (line 45 to the end) explain fully why Muhammed Ali's refusal to fight in the Vietnam War was so significant to the writer.

4 | U

(*b*) Show how the writer's language in the final paragraph conveys the passion he felt about Ali's decision not to fight in the Vietnam War. In your answer, you should refer to more than one of the following: imagery, sentence structure, punctuation, word choice.

4 | A

(20)

Questions on both Passages

11. (*a*) From your reading of both passages, what do you think are the key reasons for Muhammed Ali's "greatness"?

5 | U

(*b*) Which writer's style do you prefer?

Justify your view by referring to both passages and to such features as structure, anecdote, symbolism, imagery, word choice . . .

5 | A/E

[END OF QUESTION PAPER]

Total (60)

X039/302

NATIONAL
QUALIFICATIONS
2001

TUESDAY, 15 MAY
10.50 AM – 12.20 PM

ENGLISH AND
COMMUNICATION
HIGHER
Analysis and Appreciation

There are **two parts** to this paper and you should attempt both parts.

Part 1 (Textual Analysis) is worth 30 marks.

In Part 2 (Critical Essay), you should attempt **one** question only, taken from any of the Sections A–D.

Your answer to Part 2 should begin on a fresh page.

Each question in Part 2 is worth 30 marks.

NB You must not use, in Part 2 of this paper, the same text(s) as you have used in your Specialist Study.

SCOTTISH
QUALIFICATIONS
AUTHORITY

©

PART 1—TEXTUAL ANALYSIS

Read the following poem and answer the questions which follow.

You are reminded that this part of the paper tests your ability to understand, analyse and evaluate the text.

The number of marks attached to each question will give some indication of the length of answer required.

You should spend about 45 minutes on this part of the paper.

In this poem "Originally" by Carol Ann Duffy, the initial situation seems to picture a family journey or move from one town to another.

ORIGINALLY

We came from our own country in a red room
which fell through the fields, our mother singing
our father's name to the turn of the wheels.
My brothers cried, one of them bawling *Home,*
5   *Home,* as the miles rushed back to the city,
the street, the house, the vacant rooms
where we didn't live any more. I stared
at the eyes of a blind toy, holding its paw.

All childhood is an emigration. Some are slow,
10   leaving you standing, resigned, up an avenue
where no one you know stays. Others are sudden.
Your accent wrong. Corners, which seem familiar,
leading to unimagined, pebble-dashed estates, big boys
eating worms and shouting words you don't understand.
15   My parents' anxiety stirred like a loose tooth
in my head. *I want our own country*, I said.

But then you forget, or don't recall, or change,
and, seeing your brother swallow a slug, feel only
a skelf of shame. I remember my tongue
20   shedding its skin like a snake, my voice
in the classroom sounding just like the rest. Do I only think
I lost a river, culture, speech, sense of first space
and the right place? Now, *Where do you come from?*
strangers ask. *Originally?* And I hesitate.

                 Carol Ann Duffy

QUESTIONS

Marks

1. (*a*) The poet seems to be moving to a different part of the country. What do you think is the mood in the first three lines of the poem? Briefly justify your answer.

    2

   (*b*) Explain in detail how a contrast is created between the poet and her brothers in the rest of verse one (lines 4–8).

    3

2. (*a*) "All childhood is an emigration." (line 9)

    What do you think this line means?

    2

   (*b*) "Some are slow," (line 9) "Others are sudden" (line 11).

    Show how the poet highlights features of each emigration in lines 9–14. You should refer to word choice, sentence structure and sound in your answer.

    6

3. "My parents' anxiety stirred like a loose tooth in my head. *I want our own country*, I said." (lines 15–16)

   (*a*) Why might the parents be anxious?

    1

   (*b*) How effective do you find the image in this context (lines 15–16)?

    2

4. Explain how the language of lines 17–21 helps you to appreciate the change introduced by the word "But".

    4

5. How do the ideas of the last section of the poem from "Do I only . . ." (line 21 to the end) justify the choice of "Originally" as the title of the poem?

    4

6. What do you think is an important theme in this poem? How effectively do you feel the poem has explored this theme?

   You may wish to consider such language features as imagery, tone, point of view, enjambement, structure of the poem . . .

    6

    (30)

[Turn over for PART 2—CRITICAL ESSAY

PART 2—CRITICAL ESSAY

Attempt ONE question only, taken from any of the Sections A to D. Write the number of the question you attempt in the margin of your answer book.

In all Sections you may use Scottish texts.

You must not use the poem from the Textual Analysis part of the paper as the subject of your Critical Essay.

You are reminded that the quality of your writing and its accuracy are important in this paper as is the relevance of your answer to the question you have attempted.

You should spend about 45 minutes on this part of the paper.

Begin your answer on a fresh page.

SECTION A—DRAMA

1. Choose a play in which a character makes a brave decision.

    Briefly explain the circumstances which lead up to the decision and then discuss how it affects your views of the character.

    In your answer you must refer closely to the text and to at least two of: characterisation, key scene, theme, dialogue, or any other appropriate feature.

2. Choose a play whose main theme you feel is important to you personally.

    Show how the dramatist explores the theme and discuss to what extent the play influenced your views.

    In your answer you must refer closely to the text and to at least two of: theme, setting, conflict, key scene(s), or any other appropriate feature.

3. Choose from a play a scene in which one character makes an accusation against another character.

    Explain the dramatic importance of the scene and discuss how it affects your sympathy for either or both of the characters.

    In your answer you must refer closely to the text and to at least two of: dialogue, key scene, characterisation, theme, or any other appropriate feature.

4. Choose from a play a scene in which you felt totally involved (either as an audience member at a performance, or as a reader).

    Show how the skill of the dramatist or of those making the performance caused you to be so involved.

    In your answer you must refer closely to the text and to at least two of: theme, characterisation, stage directions, aspects of staging such as lighting, sound, movement, costume, or any other appropriate feature.

SECTION B—PROSE

5. Choose a novel which explores the nature of evil.

   Show how the writer's exploration of the theme enhanced your understanding of evil.

   In your answer you must refer closely to the text and to at least two of: theme, setting, symbolism, characterisation, or any other appropriate feature.

6. Choose a novel or short story in which the method of narration makes a major contribution to its impact.

   Describe the method of narration and explain why you feel it makes a major contribution to your appreciation of the text as a whole.

   In your answer you must refer closely to the text and to at least two of: narrative technique, theme, language, structure, or any other appropriate feature.

7. Choose a **non-fiction text** in which the writer's attention to detail is an important factor.

   Illustrate the writer's skill in this area and explain why you feel it makes a major contribution to your appreciation of the text as a whole.

   In your answer you must refer closely to the text and to at least two of: style, ideas, point of view, setting, anecdote, or any other appropriate feature.

8. Choose a novel or short story which is set in the past.

   Discuss to what extent, despite the distance in time, you were engaged by the actions and beliefs of one of the characters.

   In your answer you must refer closely to the text and to at least two of: setting, characterisation, key incident(s), theme, or any other appropriate feature.

SECTION C—POETRY

In this Section you may not answer using "Originally" by Carol Ann Duffy

9. Choose a poem which creates a sense of menace.

   Show how the poet achieves this and discuss how it adds to your appreciation of the poem.

   In your answer you must refer closely to the text and to at least two of: mood, theme, imagery, sound, or any other appropriate feature.

10. Choose a poem on the subject of love.

    Show how the poet treats the subject, and explain to what extent you find the treatment convincing.

    In your answer you must refer closely to the text and to at least two of: theme, imagery, form, tone, or any other appropriate feature.

11. Choose a poet who reflects on the idea of change.

    Show how the poet explores the subject in one or more of his/her poems, and explain to what extent your appreciation of the subject was deepened.

    In your answer you must refer closely to the text and to at least two of: theme, structure, imagery, tone, or any other appropriate feature.

12. Choose a poem which is written in a specific poetic form, such as dramatic monologue, sonnet, ode, ballad.

    Show how the particular form helped your appreciation of the ideas and/or feelings which the poem explores.

    In your answer you must refer closely to the text and to at least two of: form, theme, rhythm and rhyme, imagery, or any other appropriate feature.

[Turn over

SECTION D—MASS MEDIA

13. Choose a film or TV drama* in which a character makes a brave decision.

    Briefly explain the circumstances which lead up to the decision and then discuss how it affects our views of the character.

    In your answer you must refer closely to the text and to at least two of: key scene, dialogue, casting, aspects of mise-en-scène such as lighting and use of camera, or any other appropriate feature.

14. Choose a TV drama* whose main theme you feel is important to you personally.

    Show how the dramatist explores the theme and discuss to what extent the text influenced your views.

    In your answer you must refer closely to the text and to at least two of: theme, setting, conflict, montage, sound, or any other appropriate feature.

15. Choose a film or TV drama* which is set in the past.

    Discuss to what extent, despite the distance in time, you were engaged by the actions and beliefs of one of the characters.

    In your answer you must refer closely to the text and to at least two of: setting, characterisation, key sequence(s), aspects of mise-en-scène such as costume and props, or any other appropriate feature.

16. Choose a film which creates a sense of menace.

    Show how the film-makers achieve this and discuss how it adds to your appreciation of the film.

    In your answer you must refer closely to the text and to at least two of: mood, montage, sound, aspects of mise-en-scène such as lighting and use of camera, or any other appropriate feature.

*"TV drama" may be a single play, series or serial.

[END OF QUESTION PAPER]

2002 HIGHER

X039/301

NATIONAL
QUALIFICATIONS
2002

THURSDAY, 16 MAY
9.00 AM – 10.30 AM

ENGLISH AND
COMMUNICATION
HIGHER
Close Reading

You should attempt all questions.

The total value of the Paper is 50 marks.

There are TWO passages and questions.

Read both passages carefully and then answer all the questions which follow. **Use your own words whenever possible and particularly when you are instructed to do so.**

You should read each passage to:

understand what the authors are saying about music (**Understanding—U**);

analyse their choices of language, imagery and structures to recognise how they convey their points of view and contribute to the impact of the passages (**Analysis—A**);

evaluate how effectively each writer has achieved his purpose (**Evaluation—E**).

A code letter (U, A, E) is used alongside each question to give some indication of the skills being assessed. The number of marks attached to each question will give some indication of the length of answer required.

SCOTTISH
QUALIFICATIONS
AUTHORITY
©

PASSAGE 1

The passage is adapted from Big Bangs—The Story of Five Discoveries that Changed Musical History *by Howard Goodall. In this passage, the writer considers the impact of being able to record music.*

We are sitting at one end of a time corridor, over a thousand years long. We, that is you and I, are trying to concentrate on the dark remoteness at the other end—the Dark Ages of Europe. They, the
5 foreigners at the other end, are almost silent. Whilst we are bathed in light and colour, they are hiding from the harsh glare of the sun in what looks like a cell or a tunnel. To us they seem like children in many ways, with their Nativity stories, ghosts
10 and miracles, their unquestioning beliefs and their Gardens of Eden. If they could see us, they would think us indescribably rich and exotic.

At our end of the corridor there is a musical cacophony, at theirs a profound and disheartening
15 silence. At our end of the corridor there are a thousand different voices demanding to be heard, demanding our attention. Music has become more than a backdrop—it has become a blaring soundtrack for practically every event in our lives,
20 whether we are travelling, eating, shopping, exercising, making love or being cremated. We are even given music to "listen to" in the womb. Knowledge and information overwhelm us. At their cold and gloomy end of the corridor,
25 however, only a trickle of learning and culture survives from classical times, mainly through hearsay and deduction.

They have all but lost the flow of the blood of music. It has become for them a distant,
30 heartbreaking echo, surviving only in the keening lamentation of what will one day be known as "Gregorian" plainsong. This, the mother of our music, inherited rough-edged from the Jews, then smoothed into a musical marble, a last mournful
35 relic of centuries of joyful exuberance, is their solace in the medieval gloom. Every single note of the music of Imperial Rome, in the absence of some form of notation, has been lost. What writing is to language, notation is to music. The survival
40 without notation of something quite so delicate as Gregorian plainsong through hundreds of years of war, invasion and pestilence is nothing short of miraculous.

I am a composer. Not an important one, but one
45 who feels nevertheless some kind of ancient, almost mystical gratitude to a humble monk, at the other end of this millennial corridor. Guido Monaco, Guido "the monk", was a jobbing musical director at a cathedral church in what is
50 now called Tuscany in the early years of the eleventh century. He was charged with the task of teaching the choristers the chants which formed the backbone of the worship of that period. To my mind, Guido is no less important than Beethoven
55 or Presley, Wagner or the Beatles. He is the father and facilitator of every note they wrote. He gave us our system of musical notation. Guido taught us how we might write our music down. His solution—worried out of a bewildering chaos of
60 possibilities, like precious metal from ore—has served us unswervingly for a thousand years. I am peering into his empty room, his silent almost music-less world at the place and time of the birth of recorded music in Western Europe.

65 Our gaze now shifts much nearer in the time corridor—to the invention of recorded sound. Though the early gramophone came into being in the 1870s as a result of the desire to record and reproduce speech, very soon its principal, almost
70 monogamous marriage was with music. Thomas Alva Edison's invention of recorded sound unleashed on the twentieth century a massive amount of music in a multitude of forms; it gave music wings to cross the planet. Before the
75 gramophone age, people heard a particular piece of orchestral music maybe once or twice a *decade*. Now anything can be listened to, instantly, at the flick of a switch, the drop of a needle or the aiming of a laser. 150 years ago the very slowness of
80 making a notated score of a piece of music meant that the creator had to live with it and think about it for a period of time before it was released to the world. Now a recording can be made instantaneously, even at the point of creation.
85 Where once a catchy, impulsive melody made up on the spot and enjoyed for the evening would die the next morning, never to be heard again, now everything can be captured for posterity. And in addition, where once musicians lived and died on
90 their live performance, now editing allows them to relive and redo their mistakes and wobbles as many times as they like.

The ability to record sound has had a profound, irreversible effect on music and what we as listeners expect from it. A battle has been created
95 between the concept of music as a living, breathing, organic "condition", ceaselessly reinventing and reprocessing itself, never static, never finished, and the concept of music as a perfect thing, frozen in time like a painting, 100
sculpture, poem or building. At our music-filled end of the time corridor, have we come to love the perfect copy a little too much? Are we more at ease with the reproduction than the genuine live experience, warts and all? Has recording spoilt us 105
and numbed us to the excitement and drama of the Real Thing?

PASSAGE 2

The passage is adapted from Lost in Music *by Giles Smith. It is 1972 and the author's two older brothers, Simon and Jeremy, take him (at the age of ten) to see the first live performance of* Relic, *the band in which they are drummer and lead guitarist.*

Odd, this business of going out to "see" a band. My parents, when they were younger, would probably have talked about going to hear a band or going to dance to one, and would not have recognised or
5 understood the ritual that evolved with rock: clumps of people solemnly gathering to face the stage.

Lexden Church Hall was a typical modern municipal amenity: orange and green curtains, a
10 squeaky floor and a faint smell of hospitals. To encourage an atmosphere, most of the lights were off. Eventually, a light came on, revealing Jeremy, stamping on a distortion pedal and churning out a monstrous riff, dimly discernible as the opening to
15 "Paranoid" by Black Sabbath.
BLAN, BLAN, BLAN, DIDDLE-DIDDLE-DIDDLE-DIDDLE
BLAN, BLAN, BLAN, DIDDLE-DIDDLE-DIDDLE-DIDDLE
20 Then some more lights came on and the whole band piled in.

I had stood up when the curtains parted but was nearly forced to sit down again by a sickening combination of excitement and fear, which I was to
25 re-experience not long after this at Ipswich stock car stadium, watching a friend of the family compete in a hot-rod race.

Relic crashed through "Long Train Running" by the Doobie Brothers. They thundered into
30 "Locomotive Breath" by Jethro Tull. The evening offered more than a bit part for Fred the roadie. He scuttled on, two minutes in and every three minutes thereafter, bent over at the waist in approved roadie style, to carry out running repairs on the fatigued
35 metal of Simon's drum kit, nobly ducking the bits of splintered drumstick and the hot cymbal shards as he worked.

No one had the confidence to move around during the songs, except the singer, who had confidence to
40 spare. He wore a body-hugging scoop-necked T-shirt and a pair of white trousers as tight in the groin as they were loose at the ankles. He seemed to have learned by heart the *Bumper Book of Mike-stand Manoeuvres*. He lifted its circular weighted
45 base off the floor and toted the stand like a barge pole, in the manner of Rod Stewart; he hopped across the boards, towing it behind him; he forced it down towards the stage in an aggressive tango; he howled into the microphone and then thrust it away
50 to arm's length. Only the low ceiling prevented him from slinging the thing skywards. During instrumental passages, he maintained his place at centre stage, mouth open, nostrils flared, shaking his long blond hair, clapping in time, posturing
55 madly. It was an utterly commanding performance—the performance of a man who knew exactly whose show it was. Accordingly, shortly after this gig, the band voted to replace him with someone much calmer, who came on in a nine-foot
60 scarf and mostly stood at the mike smoking.

At five-second intervals, I glanced down the hall to see what effect all this was having on the audience. It was having very little. The place was about a quarter full. But there were three or four girls at the
65 front watching intently. They looked on gooey-eyed at this frank display of white loon pants and cheap electric guitars.

Near the end of Relic's allotted twenty minutes, Simon closed "Honky Tonk Women"
70 with a magnificent final flourish. Sadly there was still a verse to go. Everybody else, catching the imperative force of that last, juddering drum figure, had come to a halt with him. There was a pause, probably only a couple of seconds long, but
75 suddenly time felt heavy as lead. Relic exchanged bewildered looks. I felt as if I was about to throw up. But then, like the cavalry regrouping, they set off once more, ground their way back up to speed, beat a path through the final
80 verse and ended again, Simon's flourish sounding a little more sheepish this time. After that, they were gone. And no encores.

I lay in bed that night with singed ears. With hindsight, it has occurred to me that Relic were
85 really, by default, Colchester's first punk band, breathtakingly meritless. But I didn't think about that then. I thought about the noise, the lights, the leaping around. I thought about the gooey-eyed girls. I thought I could see a way forward.

Questions on Passage 1

Marks Code

1. Consider lines 1–12.

   (a) Using your own words as far as possible, identify **two** ways in which the world of "the Dark Ages of Europe" (line 4) was different from ours. 2 U

   (b) Show how the writer's word choice in these lines illuminates any **two** aspects of either our world or theirs. 4 A

2. (a) "At our end . . . silence." (lines 13–15)

   Using your own words as far as possible, explain the meaning of this sentence. 2 U

   (b) Show how the writer's sentence structure and imagery emphasise the contrasting musical environments of people in the Dark Ages and people today. You should refer to lines 13–27 in your answer. 4 A

3. Consider lines 28–43.

   (a) Explain briefly the importance of Gregorian plainsong:

      (i) in the lives of the Dark Ages people; 1 U

      (ii) to the music of our times. 1 U

   (b) Explain briefly **two** reasons why the survival of Gregorian plainsong is "nothing short of miraculous" (lines 42–43). 2 U

4. Consider lines 44–64.

   (a) Explain why, according to the writer, people today should feel gratitude towards Guido Monaco. 2 U

   (b) Show how the writer's language highlights the importance of what Guido Monaco did. You should refer to **one** technique in your answer. 2 A

5. Consider lines 65–92.

   Using your own words as far as possible, identify **five** benefits the gramophone has brought to the world of music. 5 U

6. (a) Using your own words as far as possible, explain the "battle" (line 95) described by the writer in lines 93–107. 2 U

   (b) In lines 101–107, the writer poses three questions. What do you think his answer would be to each of these questions? Justify your view in each case by referring briefly to the language of each question. 3 A

   (30)

Questions on Passage 2

7. Explain the significance of the word "ritual" (line 5) in the context of lines 1–7. 2 U

8. Consider lines 8–37.

   Show how the writer conveys his feelings about the whole experience described in these lines. In your answer you may refer to tone, point of view, onomatopoeia, imagery, or any other appropriate language feature. 4 A

9. Consider lines 38–60.

   (a) Which contributes more to the writer's presentation of the singer: **word choice** or **sentence structure**? Justify your choice by referring closely to both of these features. 4 A/E

   (b) Identify the tone of lines 57–60 ("Accordingly . . . at the mike smoking"). 1 A

10. "breathtakingly meritless" (line 86)

    By referring to lines 61–82, explain fully what justification the writer has for making this comment about Relic. 3 U

    (14)

Question on both Passages

11. Which passage did you find more stimulating?

    In your answer you should refer to the styles and to the ideas of both passages. You may make reference to material you have used in earlier answers. 6 E

    [END OF QUESTION PAPER]

    Total (50)

X039/302

NATIONAL
QUALIFICATIONS
2002

THURSDAY, 16 MAY
10.50 AM – 12.20 PM

ENGLISH AND
COMMUNICATION
HIGHER
Analysis and Appreciation

There are **two parts** to this paper and you should attempt both parts.

Part 1 (Textual Analysis) is worth 30 marks.

In Part 2 (Critical Essay), you should attempt **one** question only, taken from any of the Sections A–D.

Your answer to Part 2 should begin on a fresh page.

Each question in Part 2 is worth 30 marks.

NB You must not use, in Part 2 of this paper, the same text(s) as you have used in your Specialist Study.

SCOTTISH
QUALIFICATIONS
AUTHORITY

©

PART 1—TEXTUAL ANALYSIS

Read the following passage and answer the questions which follow.

You are reminded that this part of the paper tests your ability to understand, analyse and evaluate the text.

The number of marks attached to each question will give some indication of the length of answer required.

You should spend about 45 minutes on this part of the paper.

The following passage is about the writer's visit to see "The Jaguar Throne" which is inside a pyramid at Chichen Itza, a site of ancient Mayan civilisation in Mexico.

The Jaguar Throne

We're standing in line to see the Jaguar Throne. It's almost Christmas now and everything is crowded, including the monasteries converted to ten-dollar-a-room hotels and the washrooms
5 crammed with feet, in pastel sandals and the smell of orange peels and other things, and the crumbling hilltop temples with their inner walls luxuriant with graffiti, but this is the last chance we may ever have. Who knows when we'll be
10 passing this way again?

The Jaguar Throne is embedded in a pyramid. First you go through a narrow tunnel entered at ground level, a tunnel so narrow your shoulders touch each side, the old stone unpleasantly
15 damp, with a skin on it like the skin on a stagnant pond. There is only one passageway. Those who have already seen the Jaguar Throne push past us on the way back, squeezing us against the skin of the wall, in their hurry to
20 reach the outside air again. Eagerly we scan their faces: was it worth it?

There are a few small lightbulbs strung along the ceiling, a wire festooned between them. The ceiling itself is getting lower. The air is moist
25 and dead. The line inches forward. Ahead of us there are backs, the necks sunburned, the shirts and dresses ringed with sweat beneath the arms. Nobody says anything, though the heavy air seems full of whispers. Ahead of us, up some
30 steps, around corners unseen, the Jaguar Throne crouches in a square cubicle, its ruby eyes glowing, its teeth vivid, its meaning lost. Who used it last, what was it for, why was it kept here, out of sight in the darkness?

35 The line of people moves forward into the absence of light. There must have been processions once, flames carried, dimming in the lack of oxygen, men in masks, willing or not. The Jaguar Throne was not always a curiosity, something to see at Christmas. Once there were
40 gods who needed propitiation. Once they played a game here, in an outside court, with stone rings set into the walls. If your team lost they cut off your head. That's what the carving is, the body of a man with a fountain in place of
45 the head: the blessed loser, making it rain. Metaphor can be dangerous. Not everyone wants to see the Jaguar Throne but some see it anyway.

Ahead of us a woman screams. Panic runs
50 through the line, you can feel it jumping from body to body, there's a surge backwards: in a minute we'll be stampeded, crushed. Then comes the rumour, the whisper: it was only a spider. We're caught anyway, the tunnel's
55 jammed, we can't move, we stand in the dead air listening to our hearts, and now we know the answer: the Jaguar Throne is kept in here so it can't get out.

Margaret Atwood

QUESTIONS

Marks

1. (a) What mood or atmosphere do you think is created in lines 1–10?   **1**

    (b) Show how this mood or atmosphere is created. In your answer you should refer to at least two techniques such as word choice, tone, sentence structure.   **4**

2. Read lines 11–21.

    (a) Explain fully how the language of these lines makes the experience described seem unpleasant.   **4**

    (b) Show how effective you find the last sentence "Eagerly we scan . . ." as a conclusion to the paragraph.   **2**

3. (a) Select one detail from the description in lines 22–29 ("There are a few . . . full of whispers.") and show how it creates an oppressive or a claustrophobic mood.   **2**

    (b) In what ways do sentence structure and imagery in lines 29–34 contribute to the mysterious nature of the Jaguar Throne?   **4**

4. (a) By referring to lines 35–49, briefly describe three key features of the rituals associated with the Jaguar Throne. Use your own words as far as possible.   **3**

    (b) Explain what you think "Metaphor can be dangerous" (line 47) means in the context of lines 43–46.   **2**

5. Explain how the language of the final paragraph (lines 50–59) develops the crowd's sense of panic. In your answer you should refer to techniques such as sentence structure, imagery, punctuation, word-choice . . .   **4**

6. "the Jaguar Throne is kept in here so it can't get out." (lines 58–59)

    By referring to the passage as a whole, explain why you think the narrator draws this conclusion about the significance of the Jaguar Throne.   **4**

                    (30)

[Turn over for PART 2—CRITICAL ESSAY

PART 2—CRITICAL ESSAY

Attempt ONE question only, taken from any of the Sections A to D. Write the number of the question you attempt in the margin of your answer book.

In all Sections you may use Scottish texts.

You must not use the extract from the Textual Analysis part of the paper as the subject of your Critical Essay.

You are reminded that the quality of your writing and its accuracy are important in this paper as is the relevance of your answer to the question you have attempted.

You should spend about 45 minutes on this part of the paper.

Begin your answer on a fresh page.

SECTION A—DRAMA

1. Choose a play in which a character struggles with her or his conscience.

   Outline briefly the reasons for the character's dilemma and go on to discuss how successfully the dramatist engages your sympathy for her or him.

   In your answer you must refer closely to the text and to at least two of: characterisation, conflict, theme, resolution, or any other appropriate feature.

2. Choose from a play a scene in which the conflict between two characters is at its most intense.

   Outline briefly the reasons for the conflict and then by examining the scene in detail, show how it gave you a deeper appreciation of the play as a whole.

   In your answer you must refer closely to the text and to at least two of: key scene, dialogue, characterisation, structure, or any other appropriate feature.

3. Choose a play whose main theme concerns one of the following: power, corruption, disillusionment.

   Explain how the dramatist introduces the theme and discuss to what extent you found the way it is explored in the play enhanced your understanding of the theme.

   In your answer you must refer closely to the text and to at least two of: theme, plot, setting, characterisation, or any other appropriate feature.

4. Choose a play in which the main character is at odds with one or more than one of the people around him or her.

   Show how the dramatist makes you aware of the character's situation and discuss to what extent this led to a greater understanding of the concerns of the play.

   In your answer you must refer closely to the text and to at least two of: conflict, characterisation, theme, setting, or any other appropriate feature.

SECTION B—PROSE

(In this Section you may not answer using "The Jaguar Throne" by Margaret Atwood.)

5. Choose a **novel or short story** in which the main character faces a dilemma.

   Outline briefly what the dilemma is and go on to discuss how the character's reaction to it gives you a deeper understanding of the text as a whole.

   In your answer you must refer closely to the text and to at least two of: theme, structure, setting, characterisation, or any other appropriate feature.

6. Choose a **novel** which explores in an effective way a theme which is important to you.

   Explain how the novelist introduces and develops the theme and show to what extent she or he has effectively engaged your interest in it.

   In your answer you must refer closely to the text and to at least two of: theme, structure, setting, symbolism, or any other appropriate feature.

7. Choose a **novel** in which a main character is seen to grow or mature in the course of the story.

   Show how the novelist engages your interest in the character and his or her development.

   In your answer you must refer closely to the text and to at least two of: characterisation, narrative point of view, key incident(s), structure, or any other appropriate feature.

8. Choose a **novel or short story** which has a particularly effective or arresting opening.

   Referring in detail to the opening, discuss to what extent it provides a successful introduction to the text as a whole.

   In your answer you must refer closely to the text and to at least two of: structure, mood, theme, characterisation, or any other appropriate feature.

9. Choose a work of **non-fiction** in which setting in time and/or place is significant.

   Explain why you think the setting is important for your appreciation of the text.

   In your answer you must refer closely to the text and to at least two of: setting, theme, style, descriptive detail, or any other relevant feature.

SECTION C—POETRY

10. Choose a poem in which contrast is used in order to clarify a key idea.

    Examine in detail the poet's use of contrast and show how it was effective in clarifying this key idea.

    In your answer you must refer closely to the text and to at least two of: theme, structure, imagery, sound, or any other appropriate feature.

11. Choose a poet who reflects on the power, the beauty or the threat of the natural world.

    Referring to one or more poems, show how effectively you think the poet explores her or his main idea(s).

    In your answer you must refer closely to the text and to at least two of: mood, imagery, symbolism, sound, or any other appropriate feature.

12. Choose a poem which explores one of the following: freedom, friendship, happiness.

    Discuss to what extent the poem successfully engages your interest in this main idea.

    In your answer you must refer closely to the text and to at least two of: theme, tone, word choice, rhythm, or any other appropriate feature.

13. Choose a poem which presents a character who provokes you to contempt or anger or irritation.

    Show how the poet arouses this response from you and discuss how important it is to the overall impact of the poem.

    In your answer you must refer closely to the text and to at least two of: tone, characterisation, verse form, point of view, or any other appropriate feature.

SECTION D—MASS MEDIA

14. Choose a film which has a particularly effective or arresting opening.

Referring in detail to the opening, discuss to what extent it provides a successful introduction to the text as a whole.

In your answer you must refer closely to the text and to at least two of: aspects of mise-en-scène, structure, editing, soundtrack, or any other appropriate feature.

15. Choose from a film or TV drama* a scene in which the conflict between two characters is at its most intense.

Outline briefly the reasons for the conflict and then by examining the scene in detail, show how it gave you a deeper appreciation of the text as a whole.

In your answer you must refer closely to the text and to at least two of: key scene, characterisation, dialogue, aspects of mise-en-scène, or any other appropriate feature.

16. Choose a TV drama* in which the character struggles with her or his conscience.

Outline briefly the reasons for the character's dilemma and go on to discuss how successfully the programme-makers engage your sympathy for her or him.

In your answer you must refer closely to the text and to at least two of: theme, characterisation, editing, aspects of mise-en scène, or any other appropriate feature.

17. Choose a film or TV drama* in which setting in time and/or place is significant.

Explain why you think the setting is important for your appreciation of the text.

In your answer you must refer closely to the text and to at least two of: setting, aspects of mise-en-scène, theme, soundtrack, or any other appropriate feature.

*"TV drama" may be a single play, series or serial.

[END OF QUESTION PAPER]

[C115/SQP215]

NATIONAL
QUALIFICATIONS

Time: 1 hour 30 minutes

ENGLISH
HIGHER
Close Reading
Specimen Question Paper
(for examinations in and after 2003)

Answer all questions.

50 marks are allocated to this paper.

There are TWO passages and questions.

Read both passages carefully and then answer all the questions which follow. **Use your own words whenever possible and particularly when you are instructed to do so.**

You should read each passage to:

understand what the authors are saying about global warming and its effects (**Understanding—U**);

analyse their choices of language, imagery and structures to recognise how they convey their points of view and contribute to the impact of the passages (**Analysis—A**);

evaluate how effectively they have achieved their purposes (**Evaluation—E**).

A code letter (U, A, E) is used alongside each question to give some indication of the skills being assessed. The number of marks attached to each question will give some indication of the length of answer required.

SCOTTISH
QUALIFICATIONS
AUTHORITY

©

PASSAGE 1

This passage is from an article by journalist Angus Clark and appeared in The Times *newspaper in November 2000 after severe gales and extensive flooding in various parts of England.*

This is a tale of two towns: both modest, yet possessed of a certain civic pride; both nestled at the edge of the ocean, sharing almost exactly the same latitude. In Churchill, Manitoba, in
5 northern Canada, the winter is long, the snow is deep, the sea freezes far and wide as the thermometer falls to minus 50 degrees centigrade. There are only two months a year without snow. When the polar bears emerge from hibernation
10 they gnaw the dustbins in search of scraps. Churchill, in short, is not a place to grow wheat and roses, potatoes and apples. There are no green dairy farms on the tundra shores of Hudson's Bay. In Inverness, on the east coast of Scotland, the
15 winters are very much gentler and shorter. Cold, yes, but not cold enough for skidoos, treble-glazed windows or snowshoes to school. The nearby Black Isle has some of Scotland's richest arable farmland.

20 The enormous difference between the climates of these two towns is due to one thing: the Gulf Stream, which brings tropic-warmed sea from the Gulf of Mexico to the Atlantic coasts of northern Europe. Thanks to the Gulf Stream, on fine
25 summer days people can swim in the sea from the pale golden beaches of the Lofoten Islands in Norway—300 miles north of the Arctic Circle. In coastal gardens beside its warm waters, sub-tropical plants and exotic flowers flourish.

If there were no Gulf Stream, Britain would be as 30 cold as Manitoba. We would probably be able to walk to Germany across the frozen North Sea. Our farmers would be defeated by permafrost but caribou would thrive on the lichens beneath the snow. Dairy herds would not wind o'er the lea, nor 35 would honeysuckle twine about our cottage porches.

The Gulf Stream has not always flowed. As far as scientists can tell, it has stopped quite abruptly in the past—and in as little as a couple of years. Now 40 it seems that global warming is recreating the very same conditions which caused it to stall before, with the potential to plunge the whole of northern Europe into another Ice Age.

Which is a bit ironic as we slosh around in sodden, 45 rainswept towns and villages; as we discuss the extraordinary late autumn and give up hope for a white Christmas. Global warming was going to bring Mediterranean holiday weather to Brighton and vineyards to Argyll, wasn't it? Global 50 warming is the reason why spring-flowering iris and cistus are blooming crazily in November. So how could it turn England's green and rather tepid land into a frozen waste?

PASSAGE 2

The second passage, by James O. Jackson, appeared in Time *magazine also in November 2000.*

Deluges, droughts, fires, landslides, avalanches, gales, tornadoes; is it just our imagination, or is Europe's weather getting worse?

The short answer is yes, the weather is certainly
5 getting worse. The cause is air pollution that pours greenhouse gases such as carbon dioxide and methane into the atmosphere to produce global warming that can alter weather patterns. Whether the specific storms that scythed down trees in Paris
10 last Christmas, drowned the Po Valley last month and battered Britain last week can be attributed to the warming trend is a subject of serious—and contentious—scientific debate. But most climate experts agree that so-called extreme weather
15 events are becoming more frequent, and that the weather world-wide over the coming 100 years will change drastically. The scientists say that even if the world's governments and industries meet international goals on reducing greenhouse
20 gases—which they probably will not—it still won't be enough to prevent severe changes to the world's weather. Their advice to governments, businesses and private citizens about this is grim: get used to it.

A landmark report released last week by a team of 25 27 European climatologists confirms that the trend in global warming may be irreversible, at least over most of the coming century. That, they say, means governments should start planning immediately to adapt to the new extremes of 30 weather that the citizens will face—with bans on building in potential flood plains in the north, for example, and water conservation measures in the south.

That represents a subtle but significant shift 35 in attitude to global warming and some environmentalist campaigners are dismayed at the suggestion that the world should adapt to the warming trend rather than try to halt or reverse it.

Next week at the Hague, representatives of 160 40 countries will gather to assess progress since the

Page two

1997 Kyoto Protocol. In that agreement, governments pledged that, by 2012, they would cut greenhouse emissions to 5·2% below 1992 45 levels. They are far from meeting that goal, and the Hague conference is likely to turn into a wrangle of finger-pointing over who is at fault. Campaigners for drastic cuts in emissions fear that talk of "adapting" rather than "mitigating" will ease 50 political pressures on the big polluters such as the US and Japan.

All this because, says the Intergovernmental Panel on Climate Change, temperatures could rise by as much as 6 degrees centigrade in the 21st century, 55 ten times as fast as temperatures have risen in the last 100 years. Who will want to live in such a world—especially in some of the regions likely to be hardest hit, which happen to include those already the poorest on the planet? Dry areas will 60 get drier, wet areas will get wetter. Africa will suffer in ways that scientists cannot fully predict, but the Sahel will probably become even drier and more prone to drought and famine than it already is. For Europe, it will mean the influx of such 65 pathogens as malaria, dengue fever and encephalitis as warmer weather encourages the northern movement of disease-carrying mosquitoes. Generally, warmer water can more easily harbour cholera and other waterborne 70 diseases which will be more easily spread during frequent floods.

Some argue that the ultimate result of global warming will be a paradoxical but even more catastrophic development: global cooling. As the 75 Arctic ice cap melts, a flow of fresh water into the North Atlantic could disrupt conveyer currents including the Gulf Stream, which is what keeps northern Europe warm. According to Steve Hall, oceanographer at Southampton Oceanography 80 Centre, "One moment we could be basking in a Mediterranean climate and the next icebergs could be floating down the English Channel." It would take just one quarter of 1% more fresh water

flowing into the North Atlantic from melting Arctic glaciers to bring the northwards flow of the 85 Gulf Stream to a halt.

And in August this year, a tremor of apprehension ran through the scientific community when the Russian ice-breaker *Yamal*, on a tourist cruise of the Arctic, muscled its way through unusually thin 90 ice to the North Pole to find itself sailing serenely into an astonishingly clear blue sea. It was the first time the effects of global warming had been seen so far north.

Steve Hall's tongue may have been lodged firmly 95 in cheek while making his prediction, and certainly few scientists believe the English iceberg scenario is likely even a century from now. Some, indeed, question the accuracy of most if not all of such apocalyptic predictions. "The science of climate 100 change is enormously complicated," says Julian Morris, an environmental analyst at London's Institute of Economic Affairs. "The data are inconclusive, contradictory and confusing." Temperature measurements, for example, have 105 been taken for only a relatively short period of time and may be skewed by such factors as urban expansion. The climatological history of the world is long, he says, and man's knowledge of it is short. "Attempting to make clear assessments of what is 110 driving the climate over these much shorter time spans is fraught with difficulty." But the growing consensus is that momentous changes are coming.

Governments may stop finger-pointing and instead join hands; industries may slash short- 115 term profit to permit long-term survival; populations may realise the cost and embrace huge changes in lifestyle. Only an optimist, though, and an uninformed optimist at that, could believe that humankind will succeed in making such radical 120 changes in time to avert the bad weather ahead. So the best advice is to get out the umbrellas and hip boots and head for high ground. Storms are coming; the water is rising. We—and our descendants—will have to learn to live with it. 125

Questions on Passage 1

Marks   Coc

1. (a) By referring to lines 1–4, identify four features which make Churchill and Inverness similar. Use your own words as far as possible.   2   U

   (b) In lines 4–19, the writer contrasts the climate of these two towns. Show how the writer's use of language makes Churchill's climate seem more extreme than that of Inverness.   4   A

2. (a) Explain briefly in your own words why the Gulf Stream, as described in lines 20–24, affects the climate of northern Europe.   1   U

   (b) Show how the writer uses contrast in lines 24–37 to illustrate the impact of the Gulf Stream. You should refer to specific words and phrases in your answer.   4   A

3. Consider lines 38–54.

   (a) Explain the meaning of "stall" as it is used in line 42.   1   U

   (b) (i) What is "ironic" (line 45) about the possible effect of global warming on northern Europe?   2   U

   (ii) Show how the writer, in lines 45–54, emphasises this irony. In your answer, you should refer to such features as sentence structure, tone, word choice.   4   A

   (18)

Questions on Passage 2

4. (a) Explain how any one language feature in lines 1–3 helps to make dramatic the opening of the article.   2   A

   (b) Explain, using your own words as far as possible, why the weather is "getting worse". You should refer to lines 4–8 in your answer.   2   U

   (c) Show how the writer uses imagery in lines 8–13 to emphasise the impact of the storms which affected Europe. You should refer to two examples in your answer.   4   A

   (d) Show how the writer helps to clarify his argument in lines 17–24 by using:

   (i) dashes;

   (ii) a colon.   2   A

5. Consider lines 25–39.

   What is the "shift in attitude" (lines 35–36)?   2   U

6. By referring to lines 40–51, explain briefly in your own words two problems which may emerge at the Hague conference.   2   U

7. (a) In lines 52–86, the writer describes the possible effects of global warming. Using your own words as far as possible, outline briefly the main effects on Africa, on Europe, and on the North Atlantic.   5   U

   (b) In the context of global warming, how effective do you find the writer's anecdote about the *Yamal* (lines 87–94)? Justify your answer.   2   E

8. By referring to lines 95–113, give two reasons why the situation might not be as bleak as is being suggested by many of the scientists. Use your own words as far as possible.   2   U

9. To what extent would you agree that the final paragraph (lines 114–125) is an effective conclusion to the article? Justify your answer by referring to such features as ideas, punctuation, tone, imagery, point of view.   3   E

   (26)

Question on both Passages

10. Which of the two writers appears to treat the topic of global warming more effectively? Justify your choice by referring to such features as ideas, tone, use of examples, style. You should refer to both passages in your answer.   6   E

[END OF SPECIMEN QUESTION PAPER]

Total (50)

[C115/SQP215]

NATIONAL
QUALIFICATIONS

Time: 1 hour 30 minutes

ENGLISH
HIGHER
Critical Essay
Specimen Question Paper
(for examinations in and after 2003)

Answer **two** questions.

Each question must be taken from a different section.

Each question in worth 25 marks.

SCOTTISH
QUALIFICATIONS
AUTHORITY

Answer TWO questions from this paper.

Each question must be chosen from a different Section (A–E). You are not allowed to choose two questions from the same Section.

In all Sections you may use Scottish texts.

Write the number of each question in the margin of your answer booklet and begin each essay on a fresh page. You should spend about 45 minutes on each essay.

The following will be assessed:

- **the relevance of your essays to the questions you have chosen**

- **the quality of your writing**

- **the technical accuracy of your writing.**

Each answer is worth up to 25 marks. The total for this paper is 50 marks.

SECTION A—DRAMA

1. Choose a play in which there is a scene dominated by confusion, complications or uncertainties.

   Explain the cause(s) of the confusion, complications or uncertainties, and go on to discuss the importance of the scene to your appreciation of the play as a whole.

   In your answer you must refer closely to the text and to at least two of: structure, dialogue, conflict, theme, or any other appropriate feature.

2. Choose a play in which a character keeps something hidden or pretends to be something she or he is not.

   Explain the reason(s) for the character's behaviour and discuss how it affects your attitude to the character.

   In your answer you must refer closely to the text and to at least two of: characterisation, dramatic irony, theme, soliloquy, or any other appropriate feature.

3. Choose a play whose main theme is made clear early in the action.

   Show how the dramatist introduces the theme and discuss how successfully he or she goes on to develop it.

   In your answer you must refer closely to the text and to at least two of: theme, key scene(s), characterisation, language, or any other appropriate feature.

4. Choose a play in which one scene or moment determines the fate of a main character.

   Explain fully why you think this is the key moment in the character's fortunes.

   In your answer you must refer closely to the text and to at least two of: key scene, characterisation, climax, dialogue, or any other appropriate feature.

SECTION B—PROSE

5. Choose a **novel** which is influenced by the presence of a powerful or overbearing character.

   Show how the novelist creates this impression of the character and discuss to what extent you felt you could sympathise with him or her.

   In your answer you must refer closely to the text and to at least two of: characterisation, narrative technique, language, theme, or any other appropriate feature.

6. Choose a **novel** or **short story** in which a family disagreement plays an important part.

   Explain the circumstances of the disagreement and show how the writer uses it to develop theme and/or character.

   In your answer you must refer closely to the text and to at least two of: theme, setting, plot, characterisation, or any other appropriate feature.

7. Choose a **novel** or **short story** with a dramatic or shocking ending.

   Show how the writer creates the effect and discuss to what extent it added to your appreciation of the text as a whole.

   In your answer you must refer closely to the text and to at least two of: structure, climax, theme, characterisation, or any other appropriate feature.

8. Choose a **novel** in which the novelist makes effective use of symbolism.

   Show how the writer made use of this technique to enhance your appreciation of the text as a whole.

   In your answer you must refer closely to the text and to at least two of: symbolism, theme, imagery, structure, or any other appropriate feature.

9. Choose a **non-fiction text** which introduced you to a new culture.

   Explain how well the writer achieved that introduction.

   In your answer you must refer closely to the text and to at least two of: narrative voice, ideas, setting, structure, use of anecdote or any other appropriate feature.

10. Choose a **non-fiction text** which made you think about an environmental issue.

    Explain briefly what the issue is and at greater length show how the writer's treatment of the issue conveyed her or his point of view.

    In your answer you must refer closely to the text and to at least two of: ideas, point of view, use of evidence, organisation, use of examples or any other appropriate feature.

11. Choose a **non-fiction text** which presented the life story of a particular person.

    Evaluate the techniques the author used to make the biography enjoyable.

    In your answer you must refer closely to the text and to at least two of: narrative voice, language, anecdote, structure, or any other appropriate feature.

SECTION C—POETRY

12. Choose a poem which is light-hearted or playful or not entirely serious.

    Show how the poet makes you aware of the tone, and discuss how effective the use of this tone is in dealing with the subject matter of the poem.

    In your answer you must refer closely to the text and to at least two of: tone, imagery, theme, sound, or any other appropriate feature.

13. Choose two poems on the subject of war or hostility.

    Compare the way the two poems treat the subject, and explain to what extent you find one more effective than the other.

    In your answer you must refer closely to the text and to at least two of: theme, structure, imagery, rhythm and rhyme, or any other appropriate feature.

14. Choose a poem which depicts one of the following: the sea, the night, the countryside, sleep, a dream, travel.

    Show how the poet brings the subject to life for you.

    In your answer you must refer closely to the text and to at least two of: imagery, atmosphere, sound, theme, or any other appropriate feature.

15. Choose a poem which explores loneliness or isolation.

    Show how the poet explores the theme, and discuss to what extent your appreciation of the theme was deepened by the poet's treatment.

    In your answer you must refer closely to the text and to at least two of: theme, mood, imagery, contrast, or any other appropriate feature.

SECTION D—MASS MEDIA

16. Choose a film which has a particularly effective or arresting opening.

    Referring in detail to the opening, discuss to what extent it provides a successful introduction to the text as a whole.

    In your answer you must refer closely to the text and to at least two of: aspects of mise-en-scène, structure, editing, soundtrack, or any other appropriate feature.

17. Choose from a film or TV drama* a scene in which the conflict between two characters is at its most intense.

    Outline briefly the reasons for the conflict and then by examining the scene in detail, show how it gave you a deeper appreciation of the text as a whole.

    In your answer you must refer closely to the text and to at least two of: key scene, characterisation, dialogue, aspects of mise-en-scène, or any other appropriate feature.

18. Choose a TV drama* in which the character struggles with her or his conscience.

    Outline briefly the reasons for the character's dilemma and go on to discuss how successfully the programme-makers engage your sympathy for her or him.

    In your answer you must refer closely to the text and to at least two of: theme, characterisation, editing, aspects of mise-en scène, or any other appropriate feature.

19. Choose a film or TV drama* in which setting in time and/or place is significant.

    Explain why you think the setting is important for your appreciation of the text.

    In your answer you must refer closely to the text and to at least two of: setting, aspects of mise-en-scène, theme, soundtrack, or any other appropriate feature.

*"TV drama" may be a single play, series or serial.

SECTION E—LANGUAGE

20. Choose an aspect of language which you have investigated within a specific interest group in society.

    Identify the kind of group or groups you investigated, making clear what it was they had in common. Show to what extent the specialist language connected with the interest of the group(s) increased the effectiveness of communication within the group(s).

    You must refer to specific examples, and to at least two language concepts such as jargon, register, technical terminology, abbreviations or any other appropriate concept.

21. Choose an aspect of communication technology, such as TV, e-mail, mobile phone, which has brought about developments in our language in the last decade.

    Explain the nature of the developments you have investigated and evaluate what impact they had on the effectiveness of communication.

    You must refer to specific examples and to at least two language concepts such as jargon, register, orthography or any other appropriate concept.

22. Choose an aspect of spoken language which you have investigated within a particular age group.

    Briefly describe the parameters of your investigation. Show how far the language characteristics of the group you investigated differed from the general population and go on to evaluate the advantages and disadvantages of these differences.

    You must refer to specific examples and to at least two language concepts such as register, dialect, accent, vocabulary or any other appropriate concept.

23. Choose an area of communication in which emotive language is commonly used to influence the reader, viewer or listener.

    Outline the purposes of the communication(s) you have chosen. Go on to analyse the methods used and evaluate the effectiveness of the communication in achieving its purpose.

    You must refer to specific examples and to at least two language concepts such as word choice, tone, presentation, structure, or any other appropriate concept.

[END OF SPECIMEN QUESTION PAPER]

[BLANK PAGE]

2003 HIGHER

X115/301

NATIONAL
QUALIFICATIONS
2003

FRIDAY, 16 MAY
9.00 AM – 10.30 AM

ENGLISH
HIGHER
Close Reading

Answer all questions.

50 marks are allocated to this paper.

There are TWO passages and questions.

Read the passages carefully and then answer all the questions which follow. **Use your own words whenever possible and particularly when you are instructed to do so.**

You should read the passages to:

understand what the writers are saying about refugees, asylum seekers, and immigration in general (**Understanding—U**);

analyse their choices of language, imagery and structures to recognise how they convey their points of view and contribute to the impact of the passages (**Analysis—A**);

evaluate how effectively they have achieved their purposes (**Evaluation—E**).

A code letter (U, A, E) is used alongside each question to give some indication of the skills being assessed. The number of marks attached to each question will give some indication of the length of answer required.

SCOTTISH
QUALIFICATIONS
AUTHORITY

©

PASSAGE 1

The first passage is an article in The Herald *newspaper in June 2002. In it, journalist and broadcaster Ruth Wishart offers some thoughts on attitudes to immigration to Scotland.*

CAN BRITAIN AFFORD TO KEEP TALENTED IMMIGRANTS OUT?

If you hail from Glasgow you will have friends or relatives whose roots lie in the Irish Republic. You will have Jewish friends or colleagues whose grandparents, a good number of them Polish or
5 Russian, may have fled persecution in Europe. You will eat in premises run by Italian or French proprietors. It is a diverse cultural heritage enriched now by a large and vibrant Asian population and a smaller but significant Chinese
10 one.

It was not always thus.

The city census of 1831 found 47 Jewish citizens, a community which grew and prospered as it became an integral part of Glasgow's merchant
15 growth. The first Asian immigrants were no more than a few young men, largely from poor and rural backgrounds, whose early employment as door-to-door salesmen gave no hint of the entrepreneurial flair their heirs and successors
20 would bring to so many trade sectors in the city.

The early Italians found the route to Glaswegian hearts through their stomachs as they set up chains of chip shops and ice-cream parlours; the
25 Chinese, too, helped the local palate become rather more discerning when they began to arrive in numbers half a century ago.

All of these immigrant populations have two things in common: they were economic migrants and their effect on their adopted homeland has
30 been, almost without exception, a beneficial one. That is a lesson from history some of our more hysteria-prone politicians would do well to ponder as they devise ever more unfriendly welcomes for those who would come here today to live and work.

35 This week the Home Secretary was assuring his French counterpart that Britain would clamp down even more severely on those working here illegally. At the same time plans are advanced for "accommodation centres", which will have the
40 immediate effect of preventing natural integration, while children of immigrants are to be denied the harmonising effect of inter-racial schooling. Meanwhile, ever more sophisticated technology is to be employed to stem the numbers
45 of young men who risk their lives clinging to the underside of trains and lorries, or are paying obscene sums of money to the 21st century's own version of slave traders—those traffickers in human misery who make their fortunes on the
50 back of others' desperation.

Yet at the heart of this ever more draconian approach to immigration policy lie a number of misconceptions. The UK is not a group of nations swamped by a tidal wave of immigration.
55 Relatively speaking, Europe contends with a trickle of refugees compared with countries who border areas of famine, desperate poverty, or violent political upheaval. The countries of origin of the highest numbers coming here change from
60 year to year, depending on the hotspots of global conflict. A significant proportion of refugees want nothing more than to be able to return to that homeland when conditions allow.

But, whether they are transient or would-be
65 settlers, they face an uphill battle trying to find legal employment. People with real skills and talents to offer us find themselves in the black economy, or unemployed, because of a sluggish system of processing applications, allied to
70 regulations which preclude the legal marketplace.

Surely the most sensible way to "crack down" on illegal workers is to permit legal alternatives. Not just because of woolly liberalism—though that's a perfectly decent instinct—but because of
75 enlightened self-interest. Recently, I was reading an analysis of what was happening to the economy in the Highlands and Islands. The writer welcomes the fact that the population of that area has gone up 20% in one generation. But he goes
80 on to say that "labour shortages of every kind are becoming the biggest single constraint in the way of additional economic expansion." He adds: "In principle the solution to this problem is readily available in the shape of the so-called asylum
85 seekers or economic migrants that our country, like most countries, seems determined to turn away."

While, for the most part, immigrants to the Highlands and Islands have recently come from
90 England, the future lies in casting the net much wider. That would be, after all, yet another Scottish solution to a Scottish problem, given that this nation regularly suffers from population loss, exporting tranches of economic migrants all over
95 the world every year. It's been something of a national hobby, which is why there is almost no corner of the globe where you won't stumble over a Caledonian society enthusiastically peopled by folks who will do anything for the old country bar
100 live in it.

Yet Ireland has managed to attract its young entrepreneurs back to help drive a burgeoning economy. We must try to do likewise. We need

105 immigrants. We cannot grow the necessary skills fast enough to fill the gap sites. We need people with energy and commitment and motivation, three characteristics commonly found among those whose circumstances prompt them to make huge sacrifices to find a new life.

110 Round about now, families all over Scotland will be waving their newly graduated offspring off on the increasingly popular gap year between university and real life. Most of them will have a ball, finding enough work to keep the adventure on the road as they travel. Some of them won't come back at all, 115 having found a good job or a soulmate elsewhere. Provided they stay on the right side of the law, very few of them will be harassed by customs officials, locked up in detention centres while their papers are checked, or deported for overstaying their 120 welcome. If you're one of us and sort of solvent, come into the parlour, there's a welcome there for you.

PASSAGE 2

The second passage is adapted from an essay in The Guardian *newspaper, also in June 2002. In it, Anne Karpf explores past and present press coverage of immigration issues and tells the story of one family from Kosovo who sought asylum in Britain.*

WE HAVE BEEN HERE BEFORE

There's a melancholy little game that staff at the Refugee Council sometimes play. They show visitors press cuttings about refugees and asylum seekers from the 1900s, 1930s and today, and ask 5 them to guess when they were published. Most people get it wrong. They assume that Jewish refugees were welcomed, at least in the 1930s, with a tolerance that has traditionally been seen as a beacon of Britishness. They're shocked to discover 10 that rabid intolerance has a strong British pedigree.

And the press has persisted in peddling incorrect figures about immigration. One newspaper's assertion in 1938 that there were more Jews in Britain than Germany ever had, was plain wrong. 15 Similarly, the tabloids' current depiction of Britain as an international magnet for asylum seekers is totally misleading. Most of the world's refugees do what they've always done: they move from one poor country to another, usually a neighbouring one. 20 Only a tiny percentage make it to the richer countries: 5% to Europe, and less than 1% to Britain. A regular peruser of the press today, however, with its loose talk of "swamping" and "floods", would be stunned to learn that, of 15 EU 25 countries, Britain stands at number 10 in the number of asylum seekers per head of population.

The asylum seeker has become a composite, almost mythical figure. Despite the allegedly vast numbers of them now in the country, most British 30 people have never actually met one, making it all the easier to dehumanise them.

But what does real asylum-seeking feel like? Thirty-one-year-old Arberore arrived with her husband, Petrit, and their two-year-old son Norik 35 from Pristina, Kosovo, in 1995 as illegal asylum seekers. Petrit, a travel agent, had been questioned and threatened on many occasions by Serb police, while Arberore, an architecture student, could no longer attend the university because it was closed to 40 Albanians. "We felt that we were in danger," she says, "but it was a very difficult decision to leave because we were a very close-knit community."

They arrived in Britain on false papers. "It was very scary—it was the first time in my life that I lied like that. I felt terrible. Petrit's hand was shaking 45 when he handed over the papers." Upon arrival, they went straight to the Home Office, to tell them that they'd entered with false papers. "They didn't threaten to deport us, because we had a child," says Arberore, "but we were scared. We spent the day 50 waiting in the Home Office. I felt so happy that I wasn't any longer in Kosovo to be frightened, but I felt like a beggar that day. We had to be fingerprinted. I thought I was going to prison." It took them two years to get legal asylum. 55

I showed Arberore, now a student at Middlesex University, some press cuttings on asylum seekers. She was particularly shocked by one headline A DOOR WE CAN'T CLOSE. She said, "It makes me feel like vermin." And of another GET 60 THEM OUT, she demanded, "Who wrote that? It makes me feel as if I'm no one. I can give something to this country. But I want to say to these reporters: we're all human beings and who knows when British people might need someone's help? We left 65 everything there: we had a job, a huge house and a garden; we had a nice life. But the most important thing was our freedom."

Rabbi Hugo Gryn once said: "How you are with someone to whom you owe nothing is a grave test." 70 At the moment, Britain is failing that test, especially in its press coverage. The reporting of prewar Jewish asylum seekers is shocking because we know how that story ended. But instead of using hindsight to idealise, we can use it to illuminate. 75 Let us learn this much at least: hostile reporting of asylum seekers dispossesses them yet again. Refugees seek asylum from hate or destitution, and then run into it once more. As the daughter of postwar Polish Jewish asylum seekers, I'm 80 stupefied by how the collective memory can be so short, bigotry so blatant, and how, with all the recent interest in the Holocaust, basic connections can fail to be made. Are we doomed always to stigmatise the stranger? Must compassion only 85 ever be extended after the event?

Questions on Passage 1

Marks   *Code*

1. Look at the first paragraph (lines 1–10).

   (a) By referring closely to these lines, show how you are helped to understand the meaning of the expression "diverse cultural heritage" (line 7).   2   U

   (b) Referring to **one** example of effective word choice in this paragraph, show how the writer makes clear her positive attitude to the people she is describing.   2   A

2. Comment on the impact of line 11 in helping the writer to develop her line of thought.   2   A

3. From lines 12–26, identify briefly and in your own words as far as possible:

   (a) **two** similarities between Jewish and Asian immigrants to Glasgow;   2   U

   (b) **one** similarity between Italian and Chinese immigrants to Glasgow.   1   U

4. Read lines 27–50.

   (a) Explain in your own words the "two things" which, according to the writer, "all of these immigrant populations . . . have in common" (lines 27–28).   2   U

   (b) Show how the writer's word choice in the sentence "That is . . . and work" (lines 31–34) makes clear her attitude to certain politicians. Refer to **two** examples in your answer.   2   A

   (c) How does the writer's language make clear her disapproval of any **one** of the proposed measures referred to in lines 35–50?   2   A

5. (a) Referring to specific words or phrases, show how the sentence "Yet . . . misconceptions" (lines 51–53) performs a linking function in the writer's line of thought.   2   U

   (b) Discuss how effective you find the writer's use of imagery in lines 51–70 in making her point clear. You may refer in your answer to one or more examples.   2   E

6. Read carefully lines 71–100.

   Using your own words as far as possible, outline **three** important points which are made in these paragraphs to develop the argument about immigration.   3   U

7. Show how the writer uses sentence structure **or** tone to demonstrate her strength of feeling in lines 101–109.   2   A

8. The writer concludes with a reference to Scottish students and the "gap year". How effective do you find this illustration as a conclusion to the passage as a whole?   2   E

   (26)

Questions on Passage 2

9. Look at the opening paragraph (lines 1–10).

   (a) What is the purpose of the "little game that staff at the Refugee Council sometimes play"?   1   U

   (b) Select **one** example of imagery from these lines and explain how the writer uses it to make her point clear.   2   A

10. Look at lines 11–26.

    (a) Using your own words as far as possible, explain briefly how the writer illustrates the idea that "the press has persisted in peddling incorrect figures about immigration" (lines 11–12).   2   U

    (b) Show how the writer's language in lines 11–26 demonstrates her disapproval of the press.   2   A

11. " . . . a composite, almost mythical figure" (lines 27–28).

    (a) Explain this expression in your own words.   2   U

    (b) Explain why, according to lines 27–31, the asylum seeker is now regarded in this way.   1   U

12. (a) In lines 32–55, the writer tells the story of a "real asylum-seeking" family.

    Discuss how successful you think the writer has been in convincing you that this is a "real" story. In your answer you should refer closely to specific features of the writing.   4   A/E

    (b) By referring to tone **or** to sentence structure in lines 56–68, show how you are made aware of how strongly Arberore feels about the press cuttings.   2   A

13. Show how the final paragraph (lines 69–86) brings the passage to an emotional conclusion.   3   A

   (19)

Question on both Passages

14. Which passage has given you a clearer understanding of key issues concerning immigration and asylum-seeking? You should refer in your answer to the main ideas of both passages.   5   U/E

[END OF QUESTION PAPER]   **Total (50)**

X115/302

NATIONAL
QUALIFICATIONS
2003

FRIDAY, 16 MAY
10.50 AM – 12.20 PM

ENGLISH
HIGHER
Critical Essay

Answer **two** questions.

Each question must be taken from a different section.

Each question is worth 25 marks.

SCOTTISH
QUALIFICATIONS
AUTHORITY

Answer TWO questions from this paper.

Each question must be chosen from a different Section (A–E). You are not allowed to choose two questions from the same Section.

In all Sections you may use Scottish texts.

Write the number of each question chosen in the margin of your answer booklet and begin each essay on a fresh page. You should spend about 45 minutes on each essay.

The following will be assessed:

- **the relevance of your essays to the questions you have chosen**
- **the quality of your answers**
- **the technical accuracy of your writing.**

Each answer is worth up to 25 marks. The total for this paper is 50 marks.

SECTION A—DRAMA

1. Choose a play in which a character feels increasingly isolated from the community in which he or she lives.

   Show how the dramatist makes you aware of the character's increasing isolation and discuss how it affects your attitude to the character.

   In your answer you must refer closely to the text and to at least **two** of: characterisation, soliloquy, key scene(s), setting, or any other appropriate feature.

2. Choose a play in which the dramatist explores conflict between opposing values or ideas.

   Show how the dramatist makes you aware of the conflict and discuss the extent to which you find the resolution of the conflict satisfying.

   In your answer you must refer closely to the text and to at least **two** of: structure, theme, key scene(s), characterisation, or any other appropriate feature.

3. Choose a play in which there is a scene which provides a clear turning point in the drama.

   Explain why it is a turning point and go on to discuss the importance of the scene to your appreciation of the play as a whole.

   In your answer you must refer closely to the text and to at least **two** of: structure, theme, dialogue, conflict, or any other appropriate feature.

4. Choose a play in which there is a breakdown in family relationship(s).

   Explain the reason(s) for the breakdown and discuss the extent to which it is important to the play as a whole.

   In your answer you must refer closely to the text and to at least **two** of: theme, dialogue, characterisation, conflict, or any other appropriate feature.

SECTION B—PROSE

5. Choose a **novel** which caused you to reconsider your views on an important human issue.

   Explain what the issue is and go on to discuss how the writer made you reconsider your views.

   In your answer you must refer closely to the text and to at least **two** of: theme, narrative stance, characterisation, climax, or any other appropriate feature.

6. Choose a **novel** or **short story** in which a conflict between two of the main characters is central to the story.

   Explain how the conflict arises and go on to discuss in detail how the writer uses it to explore an important theme.

   In your answer you must refer closely to the text and to at least **two** of: characterisation, key incident(s), structure, setting, or any other appropriate feature.

7. Choose a **novel** which you enjoyed because of the effectiveness of its ending.

   Explain how the ending satisfies you and adds to your appreciation of the novel.

   In your answer you must refer closely to the text and to at least **two** of: climax, theme, characterisation, plot, or any other appropriate feature.

8. Choose a **novel** or **short story** in which a technique (such as symbolism) is used by the author and is, in your view, vital to the success of the text.

   Explain how the writer employs this technique and why, in your opinion, it is so important to your appreciation of the text.

   In your answer you must refer closely to the text and to its theme as well as to the writer's use of your chosen technique.

9. Choose a **non-fiction text** which influenced your views about a scientific or a health-related issue.

   Outline the nature of the issue and explain how the writer's presentation influenced your views.

   In your answer you must refer closely to the text and to at least **two** of: ideas, use of evidence, structure, stance, or any other appropriate feature.

10. Choose a **non-fiction text** which tells the life story of someone who captured your interest.

    Give a brief account of what was notable about the person's achievements. Go on to discuss how the writer's presentation confirmed or changed your opinion of the individual's life.

    In your answer you must refer closely to the text and to at least **two** of: selection of information, language, narrative voice, anecdote, or any other appropriate feature.

11. Choose a **non-fiction text** which is set in a society which is different from your own.

    Explain what is significantly different and discuss how effectively the writer made you aware of this.

    In your answer you must refer closely to the text and to at least **two** of: ideas, setting in time or place, narrative voice, language, or any other appropriate feature.

[Turn over

SECTION C—POETRY

12. Choose two nature poems.

    Compare each poem's treatment of the subject, and discuss which you find more successful.

    In your answer you must refer closely to the text and to at least **two** of: atmosphere, structure, theme, imagery, or any other appropriate feature.

13. Choose a poem in which you feel there is a significant moment which reveals the central idea of the poem.

    Show how the poet achieves this in an effective way.

    In your answer you must refer closely to the text and to at least **two** of: structure, mood, imagery, ideas, or any other appropriate feature.

14. Choose a poem in which the poet has created a perfect blend of form and content.

    Show how the poet achieves this and discuss how it adds to your appreciation of the poem.

    In your answer you must refer closely to the text and to at least **two** of: form, theme, word choice, rhythm, or any other appropriate feature.

15. Choose a poem which explores **either** the significance of the past **or** the importance of family relationships.

    Show how the poet treats the subject, and explain to what extent you find the treatment convincing.

    In your answer you must refer closely to the text and to at least **two** of: theme, imagery, rhyme, tone, or any other appropriate feature.

SECTION D—MASS MEDIA

16. Choose a film in which one of the characters is corrupted by the society which surrounds him/her.

    Briefly describe how the corruption takes hold, and go on to show how the film maker involves you in the fate of the character.

    In your answer you must refer closely to the text and to at least **two** of: characterisation, mise-en-scène, theme, editing, or any other appropriate feature.

17. Choose a film in which there is a sequence creating a high degree of tension.

    Show what techniques are employed to create and sustain the tension in this sequence and how, in the context of the whole film, it adds to your viewing experience.

    In your answer you must refer closely to the text and to at least **two** of: editing, use of camera, soundtrack, mise-en-scène, or any other appropriate feature.

18. Choose a film or *TV drama which deals with a topical issue in a memorable way.

    Explain briefly what the issue is, and go on to discuss how your interest and emotions were engaged by the treatment of the issue in the film or *TV drama.

    In your answer you must refer closely to the text and to at least **two** of: theme, characterisation, mise-en-scène, structure, or any other appropriate feature.

19. Choose a film or *TV drama which makes a major part of its impact through the detailed recreation of a period setting.

    Discuss to what extent the setting contributed to your understanding of the concerns of the society depicted in the film or *TV drama.

    In your answer you must refer closely to the text and to at least **two** of: mise-en-scène, theme, music, editing, or any other appropriate feature.

*"TV drama" includes a single play, a series or a serial.

SECTION E—LANGUAGE

20. Consider an aspect of language which shows development over time.

    Describe the changes which you have identified, and evaluate the gains and losses to the language.

    You must refer to specific examples, and to at least **two** of the following: vocabulary, register, grammar, idiom, or any other appropriate concept.

21. Consider some aspects of language which you have identified within a particular vocational group.

    Identify some of the characteristics of the language within such a group and evaluate the advantages and disadvantages for the group and the wider public.

    You must refer to specific examples and to at least **two** of the following: jargon, register, technical terminology, abbreviations, or any other appropriate concept.

22. Consider the language associated with any one form of electronic communication.

    Show how this language has developed and discuss to what extent it has made communication more effective.

    You must refer to specific examples and to at least **two** of the following: register, technical terminology, word choice, tone, or any other appropriate concept.

23. Consider your personal use of language in different contexts.

    Describe your use of language in at least two contexts, and discuss to what extent your communication varies in effectiveness from context to context.

    You must refer to specific examples and to at least **two** of the following: register, dialect, accent, vocabulary, or any other appropriate concept.

[END OF QUESTION PAPER]

[BLANK PAGE]

2004 HIGHER

X115/301

NATIONAL QUALIFICATIONS 2004	FRIDAY, 14 MAY 9.00 AM – 10.30 AM	**ENGLISH HIGHER** Close Reading

Answer all questions.

50 marks are allocated to this paper.

There are TWO passages and questions in this paper.

Read the passages carefully and then answer all the questions which follow. **Use your own words whenever possible and particularly when you are instructed to do so.**

You should read the passages to:

understand what the writers are saying about the ideas in a book by Frank Furedi called *Paranoid Parenting* (**Understanding—U**);

analyse their choices of language, imagery and structures to recognise how they convey their points of view and contribute to the impact of the passage (**Analysis—A**);

evaluate how effectively they have achieved their purpose (**Evaluation—E**).

A code letter (U, A, E) is used alongside each question to give some indication of the skills being assessed. The number of marks attached to each question will give some indication of the length of answer required.

©

PASSAGE 1

The first passage is adapted from an article in The Herald *newspaper in February 2002. In it, Melanie Reid strongly supports the ideas in a book called* Paranoid Parenting *by Frank Furedi.*

IS PARANOID PARENTING THE GREATEST DANGER TO OUR KIDS?

If you read a wonderful new book by sociologist Frank Furedi—*Paranoid Parenting*—you will see the story of a teacher who quit the profession after a school trip was cancelled. Some parents
5 were worried the trip would involve their children in a 45-minute journey in a private car. Would the cars be roadworthy? Were the drivers experienced? Were these no-smoking cars?

Here's another story: once upon a time, there was
10 a little boy who got a new pair of wellies, inside which, around the top, his mother inscribed his name in felt pen. This child, asserting the inalienable rights of small boys everywhere, then proceeded to go out and fill his wellies with water.
15 The ink of his name ran, and by the time the bell rang for school that Monday morning the small boy had vivid blue smudges, like vicious bruises, ringing his calves. His teacher, a zealous young woman, ever alert to the omnipresence of evil,
20 took one look at the marks and lifted the phone to the social work department. "Come quickly," she hissed. "This boy is clearly being abused."

When the social workers rushed to examine the boy and quiz his mother, they could find evidence
25 of nothing. Soap and water had washed away the dreadful bruises, and the mother's relationship with her son turned out to be impeccably healthy. The only mistake this unfortunate family had made was to fulfil society's constant, lurking
30 expectation that all children are in danger all the time.

This may be an urban myth. It matters not. A fairy tale's power lies in its ability to express authentic fears—and this one reveals the
35 paranoia that now prevails where bringing up children is concerned.

We live in an age where parental paranoia has reached absurd heights. Collectively we are now convinced that our children's survival is
40 permanently under threat; worse still, we believe that every incident concerning a child, however benign or accidental, is immediately regarded as a case of bad parenting. We live under perpetual suspicion; and in turn we project it on to everyone
45 around us.

Inevitably, this paranoia has fuelled an artful kind of job creation. When something terrible happens—a sledging accident, a fall from a tree, a scare about "dangerous" foods—the sirens sound
50 and the blue lights flash. This is not just the arrival of the ambulance: it is also a metaphor for the extensive child protection industry gearing

itself up for another bout of self-importance. Mee-maw, mee-maw. Clear the area, please. This is a job for the expert doom-mongers. 55

I am tired of these prophets of death and injury. I do not need the Royal Society for the Prevention of Accidents to tell me that children should wear helmets while sledging, because I am incensed at the thought of the hundreds of kids whose 60 parents will now ban them from sledging on the five-million-to-one chance that they might hit a tree. I mourn also for the kids who will never know the delight of cycling with the wind in their hair, or climbing up trees, or exploring hidden 65 places. Growing up devoid of freedom, decision-making, and the opportunity to learn from taking their own risks, our children are becoming trapped, neurotic, and as genetically weakened as battery hens. 70

I am fed up listening to scaremongers about the E-coli virus, telling me my child should never visit a farm or come into contact with animals. I am weary of organisations that are dedicated to promulgating the idea that threats and dangers to 75 children lurk everywhere. I am sick of charities who on the one hand attack overprotective parents and at the same time say children should never be left unsupervised in public places.

Everywhere you turn there is an army of 80 professionals—ably abetted by the media—hard at work encouraging parents to fear the worst. Don't let your children out in the sun—not unless they're wearing special UV-resistant T-shirts. Don't buy your children a Wendy house, they 85 might crush their fingers in the hinges. Don't buy a baby walker, your toddlers might brain themselves. Don't buy plastic baby teethers, your baby might suck in harmful chemicals. Don't let them use mobile phones, they'll sizzle 90 their brains. Don't buy a second-hand car seat, it will not protect them. And on and on it goes.

Teachers are giving up teaching, and youth organisations are dying because they can't find adults prepared to run them. Everywhere good, 95 inspirational people are turning their backs on children because they are terrified of the children and their parents turning on them, accusing them of all manner of wrongdoing. They can no longer operate, they say, in a climate of suspicion and fear. 100

I know how they feel. Some years ago I organised an event for my child's primary school—a running and cycling race along popular, well-used Forestry Commission cycle-tracks.

105 For safety, parents were to be paired with their offspring; we laid on enough insurance and first aid for a B-list royal wedding. Yet the event was almost called off the night before when I received worried calls from parents who had
110 been out to inspect the route. The track was far too rough, they said. The risk of children injuring themselves was too great. It was too dangerous to proceed. As it happened, we did go ahead and everyone had a wonderful time.
115 Children glowed with achievement and self-esteem, unaware of the crisis of parental nerve which overshadowed the whole day.

But so deep are we in the pit of exaggerated, irrational risk-perception that we have moved from the awareness that things might go wrong 120 to the assumption that things *will* go wrong. It is a dangerous spiral. For our children, who in reality are overwhelmingly safer than they have ever been in history from death, disease, accident, or injury, it is more than dangerous. It 125 is utterly catastrophic.

PASSAGE 2

The second passage is from an article in The Guardian *newspaper, in June 2002. In it, Catherine Bennett takes a slightly less enthusiastic view of Furedi's ideas.*

PROTECTIVE PARENTS, YES. BUT PARANOID?

It seems the childcare pendulum has swung: the principal threat to children is no longer neglectful parents, but excessively protective ones who are always worrying about germs.

5 Frank Furedi, reader in sociology at the University of Kent, has written a book, *Paranoid Parenting*, in which he explores the causes and far-reaching consequences of too much cosseting. "It is always important to recall that
10 our obsession with our children's safety is likely to be more damaging to them than any risks that they are likely to meet with in their daily encounter with the world," Furedi writes.

So, far from fretting, like paranoid parents,
15 about the risks of physical injury, Furedi seems almost nostalgic about them: "Playground areas are now covered with rubber to limit the damage when a child does fall." Should they, perhaps, be constructed from something more challenging:
20 shards of broken glass, say, or the traditional grit which was once so successful at lacerating young knees, insinuating itself so deeply into the exposed tissue that it could only be removed by a pair of bacteria-infested tweezers?

25 Elsewhere, exploring the degree to which children's lives are now circumscribed by parental cowardy custards, Furedi mentions the dramatic reduction in the number of children walking to school. In Britain, he notes, parents
30 are more likely to drive their children to school "than in Germany, Scandinavia or America, where the distance between home and school may be far greater". Alas for Furedi's campaign, some figures published this week are likely to encourage yet more of this protective behaviour 35 and may even help promote parental paranoia. A report from UNICEF has found that children in Britain are among the safest in the world: safer, for instance, than in Germany, and far safer than those in America. British children are safer, it 40 seems, precisely because so many of them are now driven to and from school.

People like Furedi seem to hanker for the time when bright-eyed schoolboys would think nothing of trudging several hundred miles to 45 school in their threadbare socks, negotiating such major arterial roads as existed in the olden days, sustained only by a few strands of linty liquorice and the prospect of a tepid miniature of school milk. Such hazards as the young scamps 50 might meet along the way—electrical storms, say, or runaway trains, or a modest invasion of Martians—merely added to the character-building nature of the exercise.

Perhaps parents who would, given a choice, 55 prefer their children to be minimally hurt when they fall off a climbing frame or into a pond are not being paranoid—just being careful. Maybe the real paranoiacs are not those who worry about their children being squashed by 60 sociopaths in cars, but those who insist on adding the consequences of mollycoddling to the already overlong catalogue of parental anxieties.

Questions on Passage 1

Marks   Cod

1. How does the story told in the first paragraph (lines 1–8) help you to understand the meaning of the word "paranoid"?   2   **U**

2. Read the story the writer tells in lines 9–31.

   (*a*)   State briefly the main point of this story in conveying the writer's argument.   1   **U**

   (*b*)   How does the writer's word choice in these lines make clear her attitude **either** to the teacher **or** to the social workers?   2   **A**

3. "It matters not." (line 32)

   Explain in your own words why the writer believes it is not important whether this story is true or not.   2   **U**

4. Read lines 37–55.

   (*a*)   How does the writer's language in lines 37–45 emphasise her belief that "parental paranoia has reached absurd heights" (lines 37–38)?   2   **A**

   (*b*)   (i)   What is the writer's attitude to "the expert doom-mongers" (line 55)?   1   **U**

   (ii)   How does her language in lines 46–55 make this attitude clear?   2   **A**

5. "...as genetically weakened as battery hens..." (lines 69–70)

   (*a*)   Why, according to the writer, are modern children in danger of becoming like this? Refer to lines 56–70 and use your own words as far as possible in your answer.   2   **U**

   (*b*)   How effective do you find the image of "battery hens" in conveying the writer's view of the way children are currently being brought up?   2   **A/E**

6. Read lines 71–92.

   (*a*)   (i)   Identify the tone of lines 71–79.   1   **A**

   (ii)   Explain how this tone is conveyed.   2   **A**

   (*b*)   How does the language of lines 80–92 emphasise the writer's feelings about the "army of professionals" (lines 80–81)?

   In your answer you should refer to at least **two** techniques such as sentence structure, tone, word choice...   4   **A**

7. Why, according to the writer in lines 93–100, are teachers and youth workers "turning their backs on children" (lines 96–97)? Use your own words as far as possible in your answer.   2   **U**

8. How effective do you find the personal anecdote in lines 101–117 in supporting the writer's point of view in the passage so far?   3   **U/E**

9. By referring to **one** technique, show how the writer demonstrates in the final paragraph (lines 118–126) the intensity of her feelings on the subject.   2   **A**

(30)

Questions on Passage 2

10. Read lines 1–24.

    (*a*)   Explain how the image in the opening paragraph (lines 1–4) supports the writer's point.   2   **A**

    (*b*)   How does the context in which it is used help you to understand the meaning of the word "cosseting" (line 9)?   2   **U**

    (*c*)   (i)   Explain in your own words what Furedi thinks about modern play areas.   1   **U**

    (ii)   What is the writer's attitude to Furedi's point of view and how is this made clear by the tone of lines 18 ("Should they...")–24?   2   **A**

11. "Alas for Furedi's campaign..." (line 33)

    Explain in your own words how the UNICEF report contradicts Furedi's point of view.   2   **U**

12. Show how the writer's attitude to Furedi's views is conveyed in lines 43–54.   4   **A**

13. Explain in your own words the main points the writer makes in her concluding paragraph (lines 55–64).   2   **U**

(15)

Question on both Passages

14. Which writer's response to Furedi's views are you more inclined to agree with?

    You must refer closely to the ideas of both passages as evidence for your answer.   5   **U/E**

(5)

[END OF QUESTION PAPER]

Total (50)

X115/302

NATIONAL
QUALIFICATIONS
2004

FRIDAY, 14 MAY
10.50 AM – 12.20 PM

ENGLISH
HIGHER
Critical Essay

[Open out for Questions]

Answer **two** questions.

Each question must be taken from a different section.

Each question is worth 25 marks.

SCOTTISH
QUALIFICATIONS
AUTHORITY

Answer TWO questions from this paper.

Each question must be chosen from a different Section (A–E). You are not allowed to choose two questions from the same Section.

In all Sections you may use Scottish texts.

Write the number of each question chosen in the margin of your answer booklet and begin each essay on a fresh page. You should spend about 45 minutes on each essay.

The following will be assessed:

- **the relevance of your essays to the questions you have chosen**

- **the quality of your writing**

- **the technical accuracy of your writing.**

Each answer is worth up to 25 marks. The total for this paper is 50 marks.

SECTION A—DRAMA

1. Choose a play in which your attitude to a central character varies at different stages of the action.

   Show how the skill of the dramatist causes your attitude to change.

   In your answer you must refer closely to the text and to at least **two** of: characterisation, language, key scene(s), setting, or any other appropriate feature.

2. Choose a play in which the dramatist explores the idea of rebellion against authority.

   Explain briefly the circumstances which give rise to the rebellion and discuss how successfully you think the dramatist explores the idea.

   In your answer you must refer closely to the text and to at least **two** of: theme, soliloquy, conflict, characterisation, or any other appropriate feature.

3. Choose a play in which there is a scene involving intense emotion.

   Show how the dramatist makes you aware of the intensity of the emotion in the scene and discuss the importance of the scene to the drama as a whole.

   In your answer you must refer closely to the text and to at least **two** of: conflict, characterisation, soliloquy, dialogue, or any other appropriate feature.

4. Choose a play which you have read and watched in performance.

   Compare your reading of a key scene with its presentation in performance.

   In your answer you must refer closely to the text and to at least **two** of: dialogue, characterisation, casting, stage set, or any other appropriate feature.

SECTION B—PROSE

5. Choose a **novel** in which your admiration for a particular character grows as the plot unfolds.

   Explain briefly why your admiration increases and, in more detail, discuss how the writer achieves this.

   In your answer you must refer closely to the text and to at least **two** of: characterisation, theme, key incidents, structure, or any other appropriate feature.

6. Choose a **novel** or **short story** in which the writer's use of setting in time and/or place has a significant part to play in your appreciation of the text as a whole.

   Give the relevant details of the setting and then discuss fully why it has such significance.

   In your answer you must refer closely to the text and to at least **two** of: setting, narrative stance, theme, characterisation, or any other appropriate feature.

7. Choose a **novel** which had such an impact on you that you still reflect upon its message.

   Explain why the novel has had such an impact on you.

   In your answer you must refer closely to the text and to at least **two** of: theme, key incidents, characterisation, structure, or any other appropriate feature.

8. Choose a **novel** or **short story** which reaches a climax which you find dramatic or moving or disturbing.

   Explain how the writer achieves the effect and discuss how it contributes to your appreciation of the text as a whole.

   In your answer you must refer closely to the text and to at least **two** of: structure, theme, characterisation, dialogue, or any other appropriate feature.

9. Choose a **non-fiction text** in which the writer puts forward an opinion which you found totally convincing.

   Explain what the writer's view is and, in more detail, discuss how this view was presented in a way that convinced you.

   In your answer you must refer closely to the text and to at least **two** of: ideas, evidence, stance, style, or any other appropriate feature.

10. Choose a **non-fiction text** which increased your interest in a particular leisure activity.

    Give a brief description of the activity and explain, in more detail, what it was about the writer's presentation of it that captured your interest.

    In your answer you must refer closely to the text and to at least **two** of: choice of detail, anecdote, language, structure, or any other appropriate feature.

11. Choose a **non-fiction text** in which the writer's ability to evoke a sense of place is very important to the success of the text.

    Show how the writer's presentation of the location(s) enhanced your appreciation of the text.

    In your answer you must refer closely to the text and to at least **two** of: setting, anecdote, stance, mood, or any other appropriate feature.

[Turn over

SECTION C—POETRY

12. Choose a poem in which the poet explores the significance of the passage of time.

    Explain why the passage of time is significant in this poem and discuss the means by which the poet explores its significance.

    In your answer you must refer closely to the text and to at least **two** of: mood, form, theme, imagery, or any other appropriate feature.

13. Choose **two** love poems.

    By comparing the treatment of the subject in each poem, discuss which you find more successful.

    In your answer you must refer closely to the text and to at least **two** of: structure, word choice, imagery, sound, or any other appropriate feature.

14. Choose a poem in which a chance encounter or a seemingly unimportant incident acquires increased significance by the end of the poem.

    Show how the poet's development of the encounter or incident leads you to a deeper understanding of the poem's theme.

    In your answer you must refer closely to the text and to at least **two** of: theme, atmosphere, word choice, rhythm, or any other appropriate feature.

15. Choose a poem in which the poet creates a picture of a heroic or a corrupt figure.

    Discuss the means by which the personality is clearly depicted.

    In your answer you must refer closely to the text and to at least **two** of: imagery, tone, rhyme, word choice, or any other appropriate feature.

SECTION D—MASS MEDIA

16. Choose a film which belongs to a specific genre such as horror, fantasy, film noir, western.

    How well did the film exploit or develop the features of the genre in dealing with its subject matter?

    In your answer you must refer closely to the text and to at least **two** of: mise-en-scène, soundtrack, editing, casting, or any other appropriate feature.

17. Choose a *TV drama in which conflict between or within groups, factions or families provides a major interest.

    Describe the nature of the conflict and show how this conflict is presented to sustain your interest in the drama.

    In your answer you must refer closely to the text and to at least **two** of: structure, characterisation, setting, use of camera, or any other appropriate feature.

18. Choose a film which casts light on an issue of political, social or moral concern.

    Identify the issue and show how the film makers illuminated it for you.

    In your answer you must refer closely to the text and to at least **two** of: theme, mise-en scène, editing, plot, or any other appropriate feature.

19. Choose an important character from a film or *TV drama whose presentation in your opinion has outstanding visual impact.

    Briefly outline the importance of this character in the film or drama and go on to show how the character is developed primarily through images.

    In your answer you must refer closely to the text and to at least **two** of: mise-en-scène, characterisation, editing, casting, or any other appropriate feature.

*"TV drama" can be a single play, a series or a serial.

SECTION E—LANGUAGE

20. Consider the language of persuasion as used in the political or commercial world.

    By referring to one such persuasive use of language, discuss how successful you feel it was in fulfilling its purpose.

    You must refer to specific examples and to at least **two** of the following: word choice, tone, presentation, structure, or any other appropriate feature.

21. Consider the spoken language of a particular locality.

    Identify some of the characteristics of the language of this locality and discuss to what extent it fulfils a valuable function within the community.

    You must refer to specific examples and to at least **two** of the following: dialect, accent, vocabulary, register, or any other appropriate feature.

22. Consider the language of newspaper reporting (broadsheet and/or tabloid) associated with such subjects as war, sport, crime, environmental disasters.

    Identify some of the characteristics of this language and discuss how effective you feel it was in conveying the events described.

    You must refer to specific examples and to at least **two** of the following: word choice, illustration, presentation, point of view, or any other appropriate feature.

23. Consider the language associated with a particular group in society which shares a common interest or background.

    Identify the aspects of language which are special to this group and discuss to what extent these aspects facilitate communication within the group.

    You must refer to specific examples and to at least **two** of the following: word choice, register, abbreviation, jargon, or any other appropriate feature.

[END OF QUESTION PAPER]

[BLANK PAGE]

[BLANK PAGE]

[BLANK PAGE]

Pocket answer section for
SQA Higher English
2001, 2002, 2003 SQP, 2003 and 2004

© 2004 Scottish Qualifications Authority, All Rights Reserved

Published by Leckie & Leckie Ltd, 8 Whitehill Terrace, St Andrews, Scotland, KY16 8RN

tel: 01334 475656, fax: 01334 477392, enquiries@leckieandleckie.co.uk, www.leckieandleckie.co.uk

English & Communication Higher – Close Reading 2001

1. (a) Any two for one mark each from:

   his placing in an attractive setting

   he was young

   he was very good looking

   he was an Olympian

   he was going to fight for an Olympic title

   he looked brave

   (b) (Whilst he looked fearless), he was actually scared of flying.

   (c) Ironic, tongue in cheek, sarcastic, dry, humorous . . . (1)

   Acceptable explanation of effectiveness/ineffectiveness (1)

   Such explanations include:

   effective as it points up the humour/farcical nature of the situation

   effective as it points up how human the young "hero" actually was

   effective as it points up how much emotion America had invested in him

   ineffective as it belittles a potentially serious situation

2. (a) This may be brief eg "Fate decreed differently." For full marks to be possible, there must be a gloss on "Destiny"—Fate/a "higher Authority" marking Ali out for greatness.

   (b) Possible features of sentence structure include:

   the conjecture/answer structure of lines 21–23

   the comparatively long conjecture "I have often . . ." followed by the very short answer— "Probably not" (lines 21–23)

   the short "Probably not." alone

   the list of adjectives to describe America in 1960 (lines 23–24)

   the pivotal positioning and/or shortness of "Destiny determined" (line 27)

   the shortness and/or balance provided by "A legend . . . making" (lines 27–28)

   the list of attributes describing Ali's personality (lines 29–30)

   the contrasting list of events which describes his life (lines 31–35)

   the parenthetical "eventually" (line 34)

   the overall variety

3. Possible contrasts are:

   once superbly fit—now broken in health and body

   once extrovert, "loud", etc—now can hardly speak, falls asleep

   once an "original"—now "just another invalid"

   once universally recognised—now so changed in appearance as to be almost unrecognisable

4. (a) Any two for one mark each from:

   he was careless/spendthrift

   he put faith in people who were immoral/were not worthy of his faith

   he was open handed/gave money away to others unsparingly

   Simple quotation = 0

   (b) For full marks, there must be awareness that Ali is perceived as a victim. Examples:

   "haemorrhaged" (line 61)

   speed of flow, seriousness of consequences

   "retinue" (line 62)

   suggestion of Ali as king and followers living/sponging off him . . .

   "leeches" (line 65)

   slimy nature of hangers-on, slow effects of their actions, seriousness of consequences for Ali . . .

   "plundered" (line 66)

   rapacity of followers' conduct, suggestion of large amounts involved . . .

   "amassing" (line 67)

   hoarding instinct of followers, large amounts, length of time involved . . .

   (c) Any acceptable explanation for 2 marks such as:

   He wanted to meet Ali for the good of others, not himself; he was idealistic, unselfish, involved in a good cause, etc.

5. Main reasons are:

   he was black in an age of widespread racial intolerance

   he changed his name thus denying his American heritage

   he converted to Islam which many Americans regarded with suspicion

   he stepped outside mainstream America's beliefs and way of life

   he refused to fight for his country in the Vietnam War

   he was a figure who actively unsettled mainstream America and opposed the established order

English & Communication Higher – Close Reading 2001 (cont.)

6.   Possible answers include:

Penultimate paragraph

"Triumph"

honour of lighting Olympic flame

significance of event in (formerly racist) Deep South

bravery in appearing in public despite physical decline

heroic situation and appearance (high in tower)

success in lighting flame despite physical problems

"Tragedy"

length of time he was seen as an outsider ("eventually")

physical decline

"Style"

sentence beginning "But . . ."

sentence structure with parenthetical "just"

word choice: "at the very heart", "emerged", "trembling" . . .

any other appropriate feature

Final paragraph

"Triumph"

honour of award as Sports Personality of Millennium

affection and hero-worship of audience

bravery of appearance in public despite physical decline

sense of duty/courtesy in meeting everyone at dinner

pride in ability to help others

"Tragedy"

physical decline

"Style"

word choice: "held our breath", "struggled", "adoring" . . .

direct speech

any other appropriate feature

7.   (a)   Any two for one mark each from:

saved his paper route money—important enough to make some sacrifice

sanded the bat—worked hard to improve condition

re-stained it dark—stained to improve appearance and/or make it symbolically black

gave it a name—as symbol of its/Ali's power and beauty

carved—crafted, some effort/ "skill" involved

7.   (b)   Possible images include:

"like the great weapon it was, my knight's sword" (lines 9–10)

"I felt like some magnificent knight . . . on the field" (lines 10–12)

"magical" (line 13)

"As if I were a spectacle to behold" (line 17)

"as if I were . . . their majestic, golden prince" (lines 17–20)

8.   Full marks may be gained by an insightful comment about one language feature, or by briefer comments about two features.

Possible answers include:

Sentence structure

the use of "But," at the beginning of the sentence

positioning of short sentence at beginning of paragraph

the lengthening of sentences throughout the paragraph

Alliteration

plosive consonant "b"

Word choice

contempt of "Some kid"

violence of "broke", "hit", "split", "flying away", "splintered"

Point of view

writer's point of view: dramatic/cinematic presentation

9.   Marks will depend on the quality of comment about the connotations of individual words and phrases.

The possibilities in the paragraph are numerous.

10.   (a)   Possible reasons for the significance include:

The writer's passion for baseball diminished gradually after his bat broke leaving a void in his life (which Ali's stand filled).

The events took place at a time when the writer was growing up/becoming politically aware/unsure about his future.

Another great black American hero spoke out against involvement in the Vietnam War validating Ali's stance.

There was doubt about Ali's commitment—whether he was a true hero and would really refuse to fight in an unjust war once pressure was put on him—and Ali passed his moral "test".

Ali was a symbol for black Americans and black consciousness, aspiration, struggle for civil rights . . .

Ali was a symbol of universal honour and morality, of right against might.

The writer saw himself as being bound to Ali, his follower, his disciple in a moral crusade.

10. (b) Possible features include:

Imagery

"drifted" (line 46)—aimlessness

"draft-dodging" (line 48)—lack of moral fibre

"the grand knight . . . dragon slayer" (lines 56–57)—heroism fairy-tale quality

"apprentice" (line 59)—pupil/learner (of magic?)

Sentence structure

listing effect of sentences from "The next . . . else was." (lines 47–50)

impact of short sentence "Something else was."

linking effect of "And I felt . . ." (lines 57–58)

parenthesis of "little inner-city boy that I was" (line 58)

repetition/listing of "I cried . . ." (lines 60–61)

repetition of "If only I could sacrifice . . ." in final two sentences

balance/climactic structure of final sentences

Punctuation

colon (line 54) used to introduce explanation

ellipsis at end to suggest continued thought/action (ie . . .)

Word choice

as appropriate

Reference/quotation alone = 0

11. (a) A listing of reasons is quite appropriate. Any of the following for one mark each.

He was a great boxer and athlete

He was voted Sports Personality of the Millennium

He is a good, warm, sincere human being

He fought against racism

He accepted his physical decline with dignity and spirit

He sacrificed personal gain for his beliefs/Vietnam draft refusal

He gave generously to those with less than himself

He became a symbol for black consciousness and aspiration

He became a symbol for Muslim consciousness and aspiration

He is a living symbol of the triumph of mind over body

Any other acceptable reason

(b) For full marks to be possible, reference must be made to both passages but not necessarily in equal measure. Reward fully any answer which presents a clear line of argument and illustrates this by closely analysing examples of selected features. Candidates may make use of material from previous questions.

English & Communication Higher – Analysis and Appreciation 2001

1. (a) Possible references which could be made to suggest an appropriate mood:

"our own country"—peaceful nature of the journey

"fell"—accidental nature

"mother singing"/"our father's name"—secure sense of family

"fell through the fields"—insecurity of moving

"mother singing"—cheerfulness

"our father, name"—concern over father's absence

"turn of the wheels"—monotonous nature of the journey

"turn of the wheels"—joyful anticipation

Or other appropriate comment

(b) One mark for identifying the contrast between the poet and brothers: the brothers are unhappy or noisy and the poet quiet or passive or looking into space.

One mark for reference to brothers' behaviour/attitude—"cried or bawling".

One mark for reference to poet's behaviour/attitude—finding comfort in her toy or her behaviour to her toy suggesting her own sense of loss and need for comfort

2. (a) Childhood or the early years are a movement from one stage of life to another.

Answer should relate the idea of a journey to movement through time for two marks.

(b) *Sentence structure* is mimetic of the different types of emigration:

"Some are slow, . . ."—

rambling sentence, punctuated by commas suggesting that emigration or the movement from one stage of life to another is gradual. "Corners . . ."

"Others are sudden"—

short, direct sentence marking an abrupt change. "Your accent wrong"

Word choice

"slow"—sense of being lost or unknown or vulnerable suggested by:

• "leaving you"

• "resigned"

• "up an avenue"

• "where no one you know stays"

"sudden"—danger, fear, vulnerability, loneliness, displacement suggested by:

• "big boys eating worms"

• "shouting words you don't understand"

• "Corners"

• "seem familiar"

• "unimagined"

• "pebble-dashed estates"

English & Communication Higher – Analysis and Appreciation 2001 (cont.)

2.   (*b*) continued

Sounds

"slow" nature of change suggested by:

- rhythm of the sentence
- alliteration of sibilants in "Some . . . slow . . . standing . . . stays" slows up reading of sentence

"sudden" nature of some change suggested by:

- strikingly clipped by short consonants of "c" and "t"
- staccato nature of short sentences

For six marks, the answer should deal with word choice, sentence structure and sound and with both types of "emigration" although not necessarily equally.

3.   (*a*)   Any one of the following for one mark:

1   because their child seems unhappy;

2   because they are afraid the child might not adapt to the new home;

3   because the parents are concerned about their own situation.

(*b*)   Appropriate comment on effectiveness of the image for up to 2 marks:

1   the tooth (the past) is still there, but it is threatening to come out

2   annoyance/constant niggling of loose tooth

3   expression of parents' anxiety having an effect on girl

4   other appropriate comment

Candidates could comment on the inappropriateness of the imagery, eg its clichéd nature.

4.   Marks can be gained in a number of ways. Comments could be made on:

Possible changes

change of time and/or place

change of behaviour, attitude or accent of poet

change of behaviour or attitude of brothers

other appropriate change

Some language techniques

change of tense—first part of poem in past; second part more recent

repetition of words summing up nostalgia: forget, don't recall, change

dialect word "skelf"

image of snake shedding skin as natural change

symbol of snake as evil

alliteration of "s" sound associated with snake

negative connotations of "swallow a slug"

other appropriate language feature

For full marks change should be clearly related to language feature(s)

5.   "Originally" suggested by:

longing for or reflection upon the past in the reflective question;

climax of longing at the end of the poem;

suggestion of origins in (the rhyme of) "first space" and "right place";

sense of loss from the past in the word "only";

sense of loss in "river, culture, speech";

lack of identity suggested by the hesitation at the end;

identity crisis suggested by "Now" or "hesitate";

uncertainty about origins implied by final short statement;

uncertainty about origins suggested by ambiguity of "Originally";

or in italicised question;

other idea justified by reference to end of poem.

6.   *Possible themes*

loneliness or isolation of growing up

desire to belong or conform

nature of "home"

confusion or "blindness" of childhood

tension between family loyalties and peer pressure

rites of passage

loss of innocence

crisis of identity

other theme or variation on theme which can be justified by explanation

Themes and language features should be related.

English & Communication Higher – Close Reading 2002

Passage 1

1.   (*a*)   Any two of the following for one mark each:

1   their world was quieter than ours

2   their world was drabber, less colourful than ours

3   their world was more enclosed, more restricted than ours

4   their world was more credulous/more naïve/simpler than ours

5   their world was more spiritual than ours

6   their world was culturally and/or materially poorer than ours

7   their world was more mundane than ours

1. (b) Marks will depend on the quality and relevance of comment about the selected words. For the possibility of full marks, reference must be made to two aspects (two from either "world" or one from each).

Possible choices include:

1	"dark remoteness"	—mysterious, depressing, strange . . .
2	"foreigners"	—so very different from us in so many ways . . .
3	"almost silent"	—world lacking non-natural noise, near music-less . . .
4	"bathed in light and colour"	—full of uplifting, varied hues . . .
5	"hiding"	—cowed, fearful, enclosed, oppressed . . .
6	"a cell or tunnel"	—place of enclosure, limitations and/or asceticism
7	"like children"	—simple, emotional, impressionable . . .
8	"ghosts and miracles"	—basely superstitious, credulous . . .
9	"unquestioning beliefs"	—unthinkingly religious . . .
10	"indescribably rich and exotic"	—materially wealthy and/or unusual almost beyond comprehension . . .

2. (a) Marks will depend on the clarity of explanation

In modern society music can be heard in almost all places at all times

In the Dark Ages access to music was extremely limited

(b) Marks will depend on the quality and relevance of comment about the selected features(s). For the possibility of full marks, both sentence structure and imagery must be dealt with and there must be a recognition of the contrast.

Possible references include:

Sentence structure

1 balanced structure of "At our end . . . at theirs . . ." (lines 13–15)

2 repeat of this structure throughout paragraph

3 listing in lines 20–21

4 use of shorter sentences in lines 21–23

Imagery

5 "corridor" (line 13)

6 "backdrop" (line 18)

7 "blaring soundrack" (lines 18–19)

8 "overwhelm" (line 23)

9 "cold and gloomy end" (line 24)

10 "trickle" (line 25)

Other references such as "cacophony" and "silence" may be seen by the candidates as being images

3. (a) (i) Any one of the following

1 it is the only music that they hear

2 it is their only link to previous musical culture

3 it provides them with comfort/stimulation

(ii) Either of the following

1 it provides the base for all of today's music

2 it is our only link to musical culture prior to the Dark Ages

(b) Any two from

1 it survived without being written down

2 acceptable gloss on "delicate" eg intricate, complex

3 "it had to survive for a very long time (without being written down)"

4 it had to survive many forms of death and destruction

4. (a) 1 He devised an effective system for writing down music

2 His system was extremely difficult to devise/his effort

3 His system is still in use a thousand years later

4 His system paved the way for all the great composers

5 Pleasure/enjoyment they have

(b) Marks will depend on the quality and relevance of comment about the selected technique.

Possibilities include:

Word choice

1 "ancient, almost mystical gratitude"

2 "humble monk"

3 "jobbing musical director"

4 "no less important than"

5 "father and facilitator"

6 "served us unswervingly"

7 "for a thousand years"

Imagery

8 "father"

9 "millennial corridor"

10 "worried out of a bewildering chaos"

11 "like precious metal from ore"

12 "birth of recorded music"

Sentence structure

13 use of short sentences lines 55–57

14 parenthetical comment lines 59–60

5. Any five for one mark each from

1 the quantity of music available to people increased

2 music of all types became easily available

3 music (from different cultures) became available across the globe

4 the same piece of music could be heard repeatedly

5 music became instantaneously available

6 live performance can be recorded (and enjoyed again)

7 live performance can be archived as part of musical heritage

8 mistakes by performers can be corrected

9 music can be composed and recorded spontaneously

English & Communication Higher – Close Reading 2002 (cont.)

6. (a) Marks will depend on the clarity of explanation.

The battle is between:

1 those who see music as something "live" based on performance—a relationship between performer, music and audience with all of its capacity for creativity, excitement, error . . .

and

2 those who see music as something recorded—the error-free interpretation of exactly what the composer wrote.

For full marks, the answer must identify both "sides" of the battle.

(b) The answer in each case would probably be "Yes". No marks given for saying so.

Marks will depend entirely on the quality of the justification

Possible features include:

1 "music-filled end"
2 "the perfect copy"
3 "a little too much"
4 "at ease with the reproduction"
5 "genuine, live experience"
6 "warts and all"
7 "spoilt us"
8 "numbed us"
9 "the Real Thing"

Passage 2

7. One mark for simple meaning; one mark for implication.
The writer selects a word which usually means a religious or quasi-religious ceremony.
He is implying that for the audience watching a live band is a spiritual experience.
Other implications, eg repetitive behaviour, routine, can get some credit but not full marks.

8. Marks will depend on the quality and relevance of comment about the selected feature(s). Possibilities include:

Tone

1 irony of "typical modern amenity" (lines 8–9) followed by description
2 irony of "To encourage an atmosphere . . ." (line 10–11)
3 excitement of "stamping . . . churning . . . monstrous riff" (lines 13–14)
4 excitement through comparison with hot-rod race (lines 22–27)
5 excitement of "crashed . . . thundered . . ." (lines 28–30)
6 irony and excitement in presentation of the "roadie" as a steel worker (lines 30–37)

Point of view

7 as brother of band members therefore fearful and excited for them

8. continued

8 as older, "wiser" person filtering his perception of many years ago

Onomatopoeia

9 "BLAN, BLAN, BLAN . . ."

Imagery

10 "churning"
11 "crashed"
12 "scuttled on"
13 "hot cymbal shards"
14 "monstrous"
12 "thundered"
10 "fatigued metal"

9. (a) Marks will depend on the quality and relevance of the argument presented. For the possibility of full marks, both features must be dealt with.

Possible examples include

Word choice

Numerous possibilities from "confidence to spare . . . mostly stood at the mike smoking"

Sentence structure

1 the definitive opening (line 38) of "No one had the confidence . . ." slyly qualified by the throw-away ending, "except the singer, who . . ." (lines 39–40)
2 the repetitive sentence openings (lines 40–48) "He wore . . . He seemed . . . He lifted . . ."
3 the listing of actions (lines 44–51)—presumably lifted from the *Bumper Book of Mike-stand Manoeuvres*
4 the listing of singer actions (lines 52–55)
5 the balanced certainty of statement followed by amplification in "It was an utterly . . . whose show it was" (lines 55–57)
6 the slow pace to drive home the bathos of the complex sentence "Accordingly . . ." (lines 57–60)

(b) Ironic (not sarcastic), Bathetic, Anti-climatic, Tongue-in-cheek, Humorous . . .

10. For full marks, there must be clear explanation of the phrase and appropriate reference(s) to illustrate understanding.

Possible answers include:

1 so technically inept as to leave one staggered/shocked, amazed at their audacity etc + any appropriate reference(s)
2 Musically poor/limited and amazingly exciting/shocking to ear and eye in the style of punk rock + "first punk band"

Questions on both passages

11. Marks will depend on the quality and relevance of evaluative comment. Answers should demonstrate a clear line of argument and closely refer to the passages to illustrate the line of thought.
For the possibility of full marks there must be reference to both passages and to style and ideas.

English & Communication Higher – Analysis and Appreciation 2002

Part 1—Textual Analysis

1. (a) tacky/tawdry
   or frenetic/excited etc
   disgust

   (b) Marks will depend on quality and relevance of comment. For full marks at least two techniques have to be dealt with.

   Depending on mood chosen:

   1 word-choice: crowded/ten-dollar-hotels/ crammed with feet/pastel sandals/smell/and other things/crumbling/ luxuriant with graffiti

   2 tone: critical/sneering monasteries converted . . ./ten-dollar/ smell—and other things/luxuriant graffiti etc as justification

   3 sentence structure: short opening sentence
   list of "and"s
   list: and . . . and. . . but
   but
   question in last sentence

   4 Other appropriate technique with valid comment relating to mood/atmosphere (eg changes in tense, point of view . . .)

2. (a) Marks will depend on quality and relevance of comment.

   1 word-choice: embedded/narrow/old stone/unpleasantly damp/skin/stagnant/ push past/squeezing/skin/hurry/outside air

   2 imagery—skin like a skin on a stagnant pool

   3 short sentence—only one passageway cumulative quality of the longer sentences

   4 Other appropriate language feature with valid comment eg repetition

   (b) 1 Setting up the expectation of anticipation or disappointment/good or bad

   2 Opening sentence with word "Eagerly"— continuing the mood of excitement or anticipation

   3 "Scan" suggests the intensity and/or the speed of the examination

   4 Drawing a line under the unpleasantness —looking forward to the reward

   5 Question form—setting up possibility of an answer following

   6 Other appropriate comment

3. (a) Marks will depend on quality of comment on the connotation of the detail selected. If the "detail" chosen is not pinpointed exactly ie general reference is made to long strings of words—it is unlikely to be worth anything.

   few small/festooned/getting lower/(line) inches/moist . . . dead/the backs/ringed with sweat/nobody says anything/heavy air/full of whispers

3. (b) Marks will depend on quality of comment showing the contribution to "mystery". For full marks both sentence structure and imagery have to be dealt with.

   Imagery

   crouches . . .
   eyes glowing . . .
   teeth vivid
   corners unseen

   Sentence structure

   climax created by fragments of direction (ahead up . . . around etc)
   anti climax or drama—"its meaning lost"
   series of questions—mystery/menace
   listing techniques building inexorably towards important ideas

4. (a) 1 processions (including torches/masks etc)

   2 gods needed sacrifice

   3 playing a game with a life or death outcome

   4 execution symbolically thought of cause rain
   Any three of the above for 1 mark each

   (b) An understanding of any of the following ideas would be worth up to 2 marks: fertility idea using blood as a symbol/use of the blood/water parallel for necessary rain/idea of the actual as opposed to the symbolic shedding of blood/symbolism necessitating the death of some participants/metaphor can disguise the bloody reality.

5. Marks will depend on quality of comment showing the contribution to "panic". For full marks at least two techniques have to be dealt with.

   Sentence structure

1 short opening sentence	—emphasises sudden nature of event/fright/ shock
2 word order in the opening sentence	—emphasises sudden nature of event/fright/ shock
3 list leading up to colon	—creating an accumulation of dangerous reactions
4 use of colon(s)	—stopping a list of possibly dangerous reaction/ setting up an even more dangerous conclusion
5 climax "stampeded, crushed"	—giving simple graphic picture
6 use of "rumour, whisper"	—suggesting continuous surrounding sound
7 lists/repetition —we're . . . we can't . . . we stand	—personal nature of the experience/almost creating breathlessness
8 colon setting up answer	—emphatic statement/ concluding the experience/suggesting danger

English & Communication Higher – Analysis and Appreciation 2002 (cont.)

5. continued

Imagery	panic runs through the line . . . jumping from body to body (stampeded)
Punctuation	colons, commas creating lists
Word choice	many possibilities

Comment on the connotational areas of any of the words

6. Ideas which might be covered include the powerful nature of the crowd reaction to something unknown or powerful . . ./the irrationality of human fear/the demand for sacrifice could be still potent etc . . ./ "the supernatural potential"/the apparently mundane and tacky or touristy actually has the power to move the emotions or spirit almost against the will/the questions at the end of the first three paragraphs are finally answered with a daunting realisation . . .

English & Communication Higher Close Reading Specimen Question Paper – 2003

1. (a) Any four of the following
    1 urban developments (accept "towns")
    2 relatively small in size
    3 same size
    4 quiet, unassuming inhabitants . . .
    5 inhabitants proud of their towns
    6 situated on or beside the sea
    7 the same distance from the Pole and Equator

   (b) Marks awarded will depend on the quality of comment about the chosen features and not simply for choosing them.
   Possible language features include:
   Sentence structure
    1 Parallel structuring "In Churchill . . . In Inverness . . ." to heighten contrast
    2 Listing of cold features (lines 5–7) and contrast listing of temperate climate features (lines 15–17)

   Word choice

Churchill	Inverness
"winter long"	"gentler and shorter"
"snow deep"	"green dairy farms"
"polar bears"	"richest arable land"
"gnaw"	"wheat . . . roses,
"tundra shores"	potatoes . . . apples"
"skidoos"	
"treble glazed windows"	

   Tone
   Informality/direct address of "Cold, yes . . ." (lines 15–16)

2. (a) The prevailing current brings warm water to northern Europe making the climate more temperate.

   (b) Possible contrasts include

1	people swim in the sea on beautiful beaches	— yet the beaches are well beyond the Arctic Circle
2	plants grow in Arctic gardens	— yet the plants are from much warmer climates nearer the Equator
3	with Gulf Stream Britain relatively warm	— without, cold as central Canada
4	with Gulf Stream North Sea stays liquid	— without, frozen in winter/people could walk on it
5	with Gulf Stream farmers grow crops and keep cattle	— without, only lichen and caribou would thrive

3. (a) Come to a temporary halt

   (b) (i) Possible answers include:
       1 the effect of global warming might be to make northern Europe a frozen wasteland—yet one would expect the weather to get warmer and/or wetter
       2 the experts say northern Europe may become a frozen wasteland—yet newspapers are currently highlighting floods, an extended summer and no snow likely at Christmas

       (ii) Marks awarded will depend on the quality of comment about the chosen features and not simply for choosing them.
       Possible features include:
       Sentence structure
        1 Beginning sentence with relative pronoun "Which" (line 45)
        2 Use of rhetorical question "Global warming . . . wasn't it?" (lines 48–50)
        3 Use of question to end article
       Tone
        4 Switch from serious to ironic, humorous, tongue in cheek signalled by "slosh around", "give up hope", "Mediterranean—Brighton", "vineyards—Argyll", "blooming crazily", "England's green and rather tepid land"
       Word choice
        5 As appropriate

Passage 2

4. (a) Marks awarded will depend on the quality of comment about the chosen features and not simply for choosing them.

   Possible features include:
    1 listing of natural disasters
    2 sounds (eg plosive "d")
    3 plurality of listed features
    4 inclusiveness of possessive pronoun
    5 use of semi-colon to introduce question
    6 use of question
    7 idiomatic register of "just our imagination"

4. (b) Reward answers which make a genuine attempt to explain the phenomenon of global warming—industrial society produces gases which are altering the balance of the atmosphere around the Earth and as a result the world is warming up

(c) Marks awarded will depend on the quality of comment about the chosen features and not simply for choosing them.

Possible images include:

1 "scythed" (line 9)—power of cut, connotations of Death the leveller . . .

2 "drowned" (line 10)—scale of disaster, death by water . . .

3 "battered" (line 11)—violence, seriousness of effect . . .

(d) (i) *dashes*
dashes highlight counter argument

(ii) *a colon*
colon used to introduce main point/ message and/or climax

5. Essentially, the shift is that instead of pouring all efforts/resources into preventing global warming, we should accept it and concentrate on changing the way we live/damage limitation.

6. Marks will depend on the clarity of explanation of any two of the following

1 many countries are nowhere near hitting their environmental targets

2 the conference could turn into a squabble about who is to blame for the failure to meet targets

3 those countries who are most at fault will "get away with it" and not be forced to change

7. (a) These effects are as follows

Africa —effects not fully known but it's likely that dry areas (like the Sahel) will become even drier
—with adverse results on crops/ animals and starvation for many people

Europe —area will get warmer with an increase in many diseases and infections previously associated with tropical or sub-tropical regions

N Atlantic—melting of the Polar ice-cap will push very cold water into the N Atlantic, blocking the Gulf Stream at times
—and resulting in frequent extremes of temperature

(b) 1 the anecdote's mention of "thin ice" and/ or "clear blue sea" at the North Pole (as proof of global warming)

2 the positioning of the anecdote immediately after mention of "basking in a Mediterranean climate" and "icebergs . . . floating down the English Channel" adds to the impact of the story

3 the careful placing of adverbs— "unusually", "serenely", "astonishingly" adds to the impact of the story

8. Any two of the following

1 the truth of the predictions is not certain by any means

2 the process of predicting weather change is very complex

3 the information available is capable of various interpretations

4 some of the data has been recorded over too short a time-scale for reliability

5 our knowledge about weather has been gathered from a mere fraction of the Earth's existence

6 other factors can affect the result

9. *Ideas*

1 The doubt thrown on the idea that governments may start co-operating and/or industry sacrifice profit for the environment and/or whole countries change their ways of living for the long-term good

Punctuation

2 The use of semi-colons to punctuate the list in 114–118

3 The parenthetical dashes in 124–125

Tone

4 The doubtful/ironic/dry tone of "Governments may . . . lifestyle."

5 The flip tone of "get out the umbrellas . . ." after a very serious point

6 The pun of "have to learn to live with it."

Point of view

7 Fatalistic, cynical, worldly-wise . . .

Imagery

8 "Finger pointing and join hands"

9 "slash short-term profit"

10 "embrace"

Both Passages

10. A case may be made for either passage. Marks will depend on the quality or evaluative comment. Answers which demonstrate a clear line of argument and closely refer to the passages to illustrate the line of thought will be fully rewarded.

For the possibility of full marks there must be reference to both passages. Reference to one passage alone may gain up to 4 marks.

English & Communication Higher Critical Essay
Specimen Question Paper – 2003

Marking principles for Critical Essay are as follows

- Each essay should first be read to establish whether the essay achieves success in **all** the Performance Criteria for Grade C, including relevance and the standards for technical accuracy outlined in Note 1 below.
- If minimum standards are not achieved in any **one** or more of the Performance Criteria, the maximum mark which can be awarded is 11.
- If minimum standards have been achieved, then the supplementary marking grids will allow you to place the work on a scale of marks out of 25.
- The Category awarded and the mark should be placed at the end of the essay.

Notes

1. "Sufficiently accurate" can best be defined in terms of a definition of "consistently accurate".

   Consistently accurate

   Few errors will be present. The candidate may use complex language. Sentences may be internally complex in terms of main and subordinate clauses. Paragraphs, sentences and punctuation are organised so that linkage and expression allow clear understanding of the writing. Spelling errors (particularly of high frequency words) should be infrequent

   Sufficiently accurate

   As above but with an allowance made for speed and the lack of opportunity to redraft.

2. Using the Category descriptions

   Categories are not grades. Although derived from performance criteria for Grade C and the indicators of excellence for Grade A, the four categories are designed primarily to assist with placing each candidate response at an appropriate point on a continuum of achievement. Assumptions about final grades or association of final grades with particular categories should not be allowed to influence objective assessment.

   Once an essay has been deemed to pass the basic criteria, it does not have to meet all the suggestions for Category II (for example) to fall into that Category. More typically there will be a spectrum of strengths and weaknesses which span categories. Assessment at this stage is holistic.

All critical essay questions require candidates to select from their knowledge of a text in order to shape a response to a specific question. Thus, obviously "prepared" answers which entirely fail to focus on the question cannot pass. Similarly, blanket coverage (especially of a poem) which merely touches on the question is very unlikely to do well.

Grade C
Performance Criteria

(a) *Understanding*

As appropriate to task, the response demonstrates secure understanding of key elements, central concerns and significant details of the text(s).

(b) *Analysis*

The response explains accurately and in detail ways in which relevant aspects of structure/style/language contribute to meaning/effect/impact.

(c) *Evaluation*

The response reveals clear engagement with the text(s) or aspects of the text(s) and stated or implied evaluation of effectiveness, substantiated with detailed and relevant evidence from the text(s).

(d) *Expression*

Structure, style and language, including appropriate critical terminology, are deployed to communicate meaning clearly and develop a line of thought which is consistently relevant to purpose; spelling, grammar and punctuation are sufficiently accurate.

Critical Essay (Higher)—Supplementary Advice

This advice, which is supplementary to the Performance Criteria, is designed to assist with the placing of scripts within the full range of marks. However, the Performance Criteria as published give the primary definitions. The mark range for each Category is identified.

IV 8–11	III 12–15	II 16–19	I 20–25
An essay which falls into this category may do so for a variety of reasons.	**Understanding** • Knowledge of the text(s), and a secure understanding of the central concerns will be used.	**Understanding** • Knowledge and understanding of the central concerns of the text(s) will be clearly demonstrated.	**Understanding** • Thorough knowledge and insight into the central concerns of the text(s) will be demonstrated at this level.
It could be • that it fails to achieve consistent technical accuracy • or that any knowledge and understanding of the text(s) is not deployed as a response relevant to the task. • or that analysis and evaluation attempted are unconvincing. • or that the answer is simply too thin.	• to provide an answer relevant to the task. • Detailed reference to the text(s) to support the candidate's argument will be made.	• and deployed sensibly to form a sound developed answer which is relevant to the task. • Detailed reference to the text(s) will be used appropriately as evidence for the candidate's argument.	• and there will be a relevant, well-structured response to the demands of the task. • Extensive and skilful reference to the text(s) will be used appropriately as evidence for the argument.
	Analysis • There will be an accurate explanation of the contribution of literary/ linguistic techniques to the impact of the text.	**Analysis** • There will be analysis of literary/ linguistic techniques and how they affect the impact of the text(s).	**Analysis** • There will be a convincing evaluative analysis of the writer's literary and linguistic techniques.
	Evaluation • There will be a positive engagement with the text(s) which will state or imply an evaluation of its effectiveness.	**Evaluation** • There will be a positive engagement with the text(s) (which may be implicit) leading to a considered evaluative stance with respect to the text(s).	**Evaluation** • There will be an appreciative response allied to a committed stance with respect to the text(s) which may be implicit.
	Expression • Language will communicate the argument clearly, and there will be appropriate critical terminology deployed. Spelling, grammar and punctuation will be sufficiently accurate.	**Expression** • Language will be used confidently and the deployment of critical terminology will add to the strength of the candidate's argument.	**Expression** • The language used will be controlled and fluent, making accurate and appropriate use of critical terminology in pursuit of a skilful analysis.
		At this level there should be no doubt that the question has been answered out of a sound knowledge and understanding of the text(s).	An answer of this standard will give the impression that it is drawing skilfully on an extensive knowledge of the text(s) to focus on the demands of the question.

English Higher
Close Reading 2003

Note that in 'Analysis' questions – i.e. 1(b), 4(b), 4(c), 7, 9(b), 10(b) and 12(b) – marks are awarded solely for the quality of comment; no marks are given for simply picking out a word or an image, or for identifying a tone or a feature of sentence structure.

1. (a) Answers should show an understanding of both 'diverse' and 'cultural/heritage' and make appropriate, though not necessarily extensive, reference.

    (b) Remember that 'positive' is in the question, so does not on its own qualify for any credit as an answer.
    Possible answers include:
    1 "enriched" sense of improving, adding quality.
    2 "vibrant" suggests they are lively, dynamic, spirited.
    3 "significant" they are important, impressive, constructive.
    4 "friends/relatives/colleagues" these are unpromising choices but might be used effectively.

2. (a) 1 Mark will be given for an appropriate comment on the structural impact (e.g. dramatic, emphatic....) which derives from:
    1 the brevity of the sentence;
    2 the fact that it constitutes a paragraph in itself;
    3 its near mono-syllabic nature
    and 1 Mark for acknowledging the "now and then" contrast between the first and third paragraphs.

3. (a) Similarities between Jewish and Asian immigrants to Glasgow could include:
    1 they were initially few in number
    2 they have been (very) successful in business or commerce (that they became rich alone is insufficient as a similarity)
    3 they contributed to the community (financially and/or culturally)

    (b) A similarity between Italian and Chinese immigrants could be that
    they introduced new food/eating habits
    OR
    they changed attitudes to food/eating

4. (a) 1 gloss on "economic (migrants)"
    2 gloss on "beneficial"
    3 they have been vilified by some politicians
    4 they have been exposed to dicriminatory treatment
    5 they have been exploited by those who arrange illegal entry

4. (b) Possible answers include:
    1 "lesson" implies need for instruction/improvement
    2 "hysteria-prone" sense of frenzied behaviour, implication of stirring up others' emotions
    3 "ponder" implies their normal course of action lacks thought
    4 "devise" sense of scheming
    5 "(ever more) unfriendly" antagonistic attitude
    6 "ever more" sense of their relentlessness
    7 "would do well" judgemental tone

    (c) Possible areas for comment include:
    Word choice/imagery
    1 "clamp down" (lines 36–37) violent, aggressive, restrictive
    2 "immediate" (line 40) sudden imposition of restraint
    3 "preventing" (line 40) negative connotations of holding back
    4 "denied" (line 42) negative connotations of refusal
    5 "stem" (line 44) idea of blocking up, preventing natural movement/growth
    6 "clinging" (line 45) emphasises dangerous nature of action to which they are driven
    7 "obscene" (line 47) extreme distaste.
    (6 & 7 are relevant only if they are seen as consequences of Government action)
    Tone
    8 sympathetic – justified by, e.g. "preventing natural integration", "harmonising effect",...
    9 angry – justified by, e.g. "risk their lives", "obscene sums", "traffikers of human misery"...
    10 ironic/euphemistic – justified by, e.g. use of inverted commas around "accommodation centres".
    Structure
    11 "This week...At the same time... Meanwhile" gives a sense of immediacy.
    12 climactic structure of the final sentence.

5. (a) Four elements are required:
    1 'this (ever more draconian) approach'...
    2 ..refers to the (harsh) proposals in the previous paragraph
    3 '(a number of) misconceptions'...
    4 ...leads into the muddled ideas to be looked at in this paragraph

    Reference to 'Yet' could be made as the indicator of movement from the restrictive measures to the muddled ideas.

    (b) Possible references include:
    1 "heart" (line 51)
    2 "swamped by a tidal wave" (line 54)
    3 "trickle" (line 56)
    4 "hotspots" (line 60)
    5 "uphill battle" (line 65)
    6 "legal marketplace" (line 70)
    Notice could be taken of the rather clichéd nature of some of the images.

6.
1 We should permit/encourage immigration
2 This is in line with our humane/inclusive tradition
3 It would be to our own economic advantage
4 The economy of the Highlands and Islands would benefit/it would solve the shortage of suitable workers
5 We should encourage new residents not just from England/seek greater diversity
6 Scots have emigrated to many places in the past

7. Possible references/comments:
Sentence structure
1 Repeated pattern in "We must…" "We need…" passionate, rhetorical, exhortatory
2 Repetition of "we" sense of collective responsibility, involvement
3 expanding length of second to fifth sentences suggests increasing passion, anger
4 use of "…and…and…" – build-up of enthusiasm, commitment
5 use of short sentence(s) – impact, urgency, bluntness, rhetoric
Tone
6 admiring, uplifting, urgent, hectoring – "energy… commitment…motivation… sacrifice".

8. It can be argued that the conclusion is effective or ineffective.
Reference could be made to one or more of the following:
1 relevance to themselves as young people/students
2 topicality
3 contrast between the ease with which these Scottish students are accepted abroad and the difficulties faced by many coming to the UK/Scotland
4 the informal tone contrasted with the serious/concerned impassioned tone earlier
5 the caustic tone of the final sentence
6 the effective use of a specific example
7 the way the illustration turns the tables on ourselves/points up our hypocrisy
8 the sudden leap to an apparently new topic.

9. (a)1 to show that racism/prejudiced press coverage is not new
2 to make people re-think their attitude to racism
3 to subvert visitors' preconceptions about (press coverage of) race
4 to show people they have wrong ideas (about immigration/race)

(b)1 "beacon of Britishness" (line 9)
idea of pride, shining light, guiding light, …
2 "rabid intolerance" (line 10)
implying that it is frightening, virulent, diseased, …
3 "pedigree" (line 10)
suggesting a distinguished history, that ironically we're proud of it, …
4 "game" (line 1)
unpromising choice, but might just be used with some success

10. (a)Answers could deal with one or more of the following:
1 the "incorrect figures", which are illustrated by the reference to the number of Jews in Britain and/or the failure to acknowledge both the tiny percentage of refugees who come to Britain and Britain's true position relative to other EU countries.
2 the idea of "has persisted", which is illustrated by referring to "1938" and to "today" or "current".
3 the tone of "peddling", which suggests underhand, dishonest dealing and is developed in, for example, "assertion … depiction … loose talk".

(b)Comment could be on any of the following:
1 "persisted"
2 "peddling"
3 "assertion"
4 "plain wrong"
5 "(totally) misleading"
6 "loose talk"
7 "swamping" [connotation and/or use of inverted commas]
8 "floods" [connotation and/or use of inverted commas]
9 "stunned"
10 other choices, or answers on features such as sentence structure, punctuation or alliteration.

11. (a)gloss on "composite"
gloss on "mythical"

(b)The key point is "most British people have never actually met one".

12. (a)There must be clear identification (and, where appropriate, exemplification) of more than one technique which, in the candidate's eyes, allows the writer to present Arberore's story as a plausible piece of narrative.
Lengthy and/or unfocussed quotation or mere paraphrase will be a serious fault, as will over-reliance on Arberore's words rather than on the writer's techniques.

Reference could be made to:
1 use of real, named people – Arberore, Petrit, Norik
2 use of specific places – Pristina, Kosovo
3 use of exact ages, in the style of newspapers
4 use of specific year – 1995
5 giving details of job/occupation – travel agent, student
6 use of dialogue/direct quotation
7 use of present tense – "says"
8 use of sequential narrative – "they arrived … upon arrival …".

English Higher
Close Reading 2003 (cont.)

12. (b) Possible references:

   Tone:
   1 "vermin" (line 60) – outraged, ...
   2 "all human beings" (line 64) – dignified, ...
   3 "who knows when" (line 64) – accusatory, ...
   4 "freedom" (line 68) – sincere, ...

   Sentence Structure:
   5 preponderance of simple, heartfelt sentences
   6 "But ..." (line 63)
   7 structure of sentence beginning "We left ...."
      (lines 65–67)
   8 the repetition: "we", "makes me feel"
   9 the accusatory question "Who wrote that?"
      (line 61) [not rhetorical]
   10 the rhetorical question (lines 64–65)

13. *Ideas:*
   1 mention of the Holocaust
   2 the writer's revelation of her own background
   3 Rabbi Gryn's statement
   4 the depth of her sympathy for asylum seekers
   Language/style:
   5 intensity of "shocking... stupefied..." (lines 73, 81)
   6 harsh connotations of "dispossesses ... destitute ... hate" (lines 77–78)
   7 rhetorical flourish in "so short ... so blatant ..." (lines 81–82)
   8 harsh alliteration in "bigotry so blatant" (line 82)
   9 prayer-like "let us learn" (line 76)
   10 use of (rhetorical) questions (lines 84–86)
   11 any other valid point

14. Note that the question is on "issues" and "ideas", not language or style. While it will not be wholly inappropriate to refer to, for example, emotional language, the thrust of the answer must address the writers' ideas.

   There must be comparison between the passages, but candidates may choose to focus more on the ideas of one passage.

English Higher
Critical Essay 2003

Please refer to the answer guidelines given for the Critical Essay in the English & Communication Higher Specimen Question Paper – 2003.

English Higher
Close Reading
2004

Note that in 'Analysis' questions – i.e. 2(b), 4(a), 4(b)(ii), 5(b), 6, 9, 10(a), 10(c)(ii), 12 – marks are awarded solely for the quality of comment; no marks are given for simply picking out a word or an image, or for identifying a tone or a feature of sentence structure.

1. 1 (unnecessarily) fearful, worried, concerned, (over) anxious
   2 suspicious of everyone / everything
   3 always fearing the worst
   4 unable to leave the children to their own devices
   1 mark will also be given for appropriate reference to parents' questions, worries, concerns.

2. (a) The story shows that:
   1 an apparently serious incident had an innocent explanation
   2 people are too ready to rush to judgement
   3 rushing to judgement is wrong
   4 teacher / social workers / authorities misinterpreted the situation
   5 teacher / social workers / authorities were made to look foolish
   6 it is a further example of "paranoia"
   7 it is a feature of our age
   8 other appropriate answer

   (b) *Teacher:*
   1 "zealous" (line 18)
      suggests over-enthusiastic, fanatical, driven by personal agenda, ...
   2 "ever alert" (line 19)
      slightly mocking, suggesting keenness to find fault, ...
   3 "omnipresence" (line 19)
      exaggeration
   4 "one look" (line 20)
      emphasises precipitate action
   5 "hissed" (line 22)
      suggests vicious, spiteful, animal-like, ...
   6 "clearly" (line 22)
      shows certainty, lack of any doubt, ...

   Social Workers:
   7 "rushed" (line 23)
      speed, lack of deliberation, ...
   8 "quiz" (line 24)
      suggestion of intrusive questioning, ...

   Either:
   9 "once upon a time" (line 9)
      suggests living in fantasy / fairy-tale world

3. Marks will be awarded for:
   1. a clear understanding of "A fairy tale's power lies in its ability to express authentic fears" – e.g. the impact of such a story comes from the way it can articulate real worries
      and / or

2. a clear understanding of: "...this one reveals the paranoia that now prevails ..." – e.g. such a story exposes the irrational fears which are widespread
and / or

3. a clear understanding of "urban myth" as an articulation of real fears.

4. (a) Possible answers include:
Word choice:
1 "permanently ... worse still... every ... immediately ... perpetual ... everyone" concentration of intensifying words

2 "threat ... bad ... suspicion" connotations of danger, evil

Sentence structure:
3 repetition of "we" / "we live" rhetorical / emotional device; sense of inclusiveness; demonstrates extent of problem

4 positioning of "Collectively" to intensify universality

5 the two sentences from "Collectively ..." to "... us." contain a number of relevant features (e.g. climax, balancing round semi-colon, ...) and appropriate comment could be made on any of these

Sound:
6 alliteration of "Collectively" and "convinced" contains a hint of (self-)mockery

Imagery:
7 "absurd heights" it will not be easy to make appropriate comment since this is in the question, but it might be possible

(b) (i) contempt, mockery, disapproval, anger, ...

(ii) Possible answers include:
1 "paranoia" (line 46) implies their behaviour is irrational, ...
2 "artful" (line 46) implies they're self-serving, sly, ...
3 "something terrible" (line 47) ironic tone – examples are fairly innocuous
4 inverted commas at "dangerous" (line 49) to point up falseness, exaggeration, implication they're not dangerous at all
5 "sirens / blue lights"(lines 49–50) over-reaction, trivializing as a spectacle, assumption of guilt
6 "industry" (line 52) suggests organized nature, large scale, empire-building, profit-making
7 "(bout of) self-importance" (line 53) accuses them of taking themselves too seriously
8 "Mee-maw, mee-maw." (line 54) imitation of the sound suggests they are childish, ...

4. (b) (ii) continued
9 "Clear the area, please." (line 54) paints them as authoritarian, overbearing, pushy...
10 "expert" (line 55) perhaps people who call themselves "experts" are not to be trusted
11 "doom-mongers" (line 55) as if tragedy / injury is their living, they thrive on it, ...

5. (a) A good gloss of "devoid of freedom, decision-making, and the opportunity to take their own risks" will gain marks.
Alternatively, a more general summary of the paragraph along the lines of "They are being denied experiences from the 'real' world" will also gain marks.
Excessive use of the concrete (e.g. references to helmets, sledging, cycling, trees, etc) rather than the abstract will constitute a weakness.

(b) For full marks an answer must make clear the root and the implication of the image (that the unnatural, restricted, unhealthy, cruel environment in which battery hens are raised is being compared with the way children today are being denied real, healthy, risky experiences) and make some evaluative comment.

6. (a) (i) anger, contempt, frustration, ...
get: tired, bored, weary, ...

(ii) Possible answers:
1 repetitive structure of "I'm fed up ... I am weary ... I am sick ..." drives home the point forcefully
2 word choice in "fed up ... weary ... sick" exaggerated connotations of illness, depression, ...
3 word choice in "scaremongers"/"lurk" connotation of threat
4 use of intensifiers: "never ... everywhere ... never" emphatic, strong personal commitment
5 balancing of "on the one hand ... at the same time" points up the contradictory, illogical attitude

(b) Possible answers:
Sentence structure:
1 positioning of "Everywhere" (line 80) emphatic exaggeration
2 the parenthesis about the media (line 81) sneering tone
3 the string of sentences beginning "Don't ..." (lines 83-92) emphasises their negative, authoritarian attitude
4 the repeated structure of command followed by reason (line 83-91) as above, or emphasises the weak justifications (in writer's eyes)
5 "And on and on it goes." (line 92) deliberately glib, repetitive, ...

English Higher
Close Reading
2004 (cont.)

6. (b) continued

Tone:

6 "ably abetted" (line 81)
   sarcastic, sneering

7 "hard at work" (lines 81-82)
   ironic – she doesn't value their work at all

8 "brain themselves" (lines 87-88)
   use of colloquialism for humour

9 "sizzle their brains" (lines 90-91)
   use of exaggeration, colloquialism for humour

10 "And on and on it goes" (line 92)
   (mock) weariness, distaste, ...

Word choice:

11 "army" (line 80)
   large numbers, organised, overwhelming, threatening, ...

12 "abetted" (line 81)
   suggests underhand activity, criminality, ...

7. Any two of the following could be included in a good answer:

1 they are frightened of accusation (from parents and / or children)

2 they are unable to give their best

3 the atmosphere is not conducive to helping young people

8. In a good answer candidates will show a clear grasp of the key idea that despite the worries of some (paranoid) parents, the trip was a success. They should also show, with appropriate reference, how effectively (or not) this supports the thrust of her argument in the article thus far.

Note that the question refers to ideas, not style or language, although it is possible that these may be used appropriately to support candidates' comments on the anecdote.

9. Possible answers:

Word choice / imagery:

1 "pit"
   suggestion of low, dark, murky, infernal, ...

2 "exaggerated"
   suggestion of illogical, unfounded, ...

3 "irrational"
   suggestion of mental weakness, ...

4 "spiral"
   suggestion of being out of control, ...

5 "overwhelmingly"
   suggestion of something devastating, crushing, ...

6 "utterly"
   very emphatic, hint of despair, ...

7 "catastrophic"
   as big a disaster as can be imagined, ...

Sentence structure:

8 "But so deep are we ..."
   inversion for rhetorical effect, emphasis on "deep"

9 balance of "might go wrong ... *will* go wrong" rhetorical (also use of italics just in case the point is missed)

10 the brevity of "It is a dangerous spiral" and / or "It is utterly catastrophic"
   emphatic

11 the repetition of "It is ..."
   preachy, hectoring, ...

12 the listing of "... death, disease, accident, or injury ..."
   to emphasise the range of threats nowadays reduced

13 the intrusive parenthesis in "For.. dangerous" delaying the main clause
   dramatic, rhetorical, ...

14 brevity of "It is utterly catastrophic."
   emphatic conclusion

Tone:

15 anger, despair, moral superiority, established by almost any of the above

10. (a) A good answer should include the straightforward explanation that a pendulum swings from one extreme / side to the other, as have views on how to care for children.

(b) Answers should include the meaning of the word "cosseting": e.g. pamper, over-protect, spoil, ...
Reference should also be made to or explanation of context, e.g.
1 "excessively protective"
2 "always worrying (about germs)"
3 "obsession with our child's safety"
4 "playing areas covered with rubber"
5 *Paranoid Parenting*

(c) (i) Answers can include any of the following:
   1 they are not dangerous enough
   2 they shouldn't be protected (with rubber)
   3 they are too safe

(ii) One mark for defining attitude, e.g. it is wrong, stupid, dangerous, ...
   One mark for observing / illustrating that the (humorous) exaggeration makes the tone sarcastic, mocking, ...

11. Answers should refer to both sides of the argument:
Furedi wishes a reduction in car journeys to school or thinks that it is bad for children to be driven to school.
UNICEF figures show that this actually makes them safer.

12. A good answer will pick up on the mocking, derisory attitude developed through the wild exaggeration or tongue-in-cheek tone. This should be supported with appropriate (ideally succinct) references.

13. The following two points would constitute an ideal answer:
1 parents who look after or are concerned for their children aren't doing anything wrong
2 those who criticise parents for being protective are adding to parents' worries

14. Note that the question is on "ideas", not language or style. While it will not be wholly inappropriate for candidates to refer to, for example, Reid's rhetoric and / or Bennett's humour, the thrust of the answer must address the writers' ideas about Furedi and his beliefs.
A good answer will have a clear and intelligent understanding of both passages, including evaluative comments that are thoughtful and convincing.

English Higher
Critical Essay
2004

Please refer to the answer guidelines given for the Critical Essay in the English & Communication Higher Specimen Question Paper – 2003.

Official SQA answers to 1-84372-237-2
2001, 2002, 2003 SQP, 2003 and 2004